CORNWAI
GEOLOGICAL HI

Peter Stanier

Granite rocks at Stowe's Hill

Cornwall's peninsula offers a remarkable wealth of geology. This is especially true of its minerals, some of which are very rare and world-famous. A wide variety of rock types has determined the coastal and inland scenery, which in turn has influenced man's activities such as farming, seafaring and the extractive industries. Cornwall's granites and slates are well known, and china clay workings have created a unique landscape around St Austell. Tin, copper, lead, zinc and other metals were the mainstay of a once productive mining industry, for which there is abundant evidence in the form of abandoned engine houses, shafts and overgrown waste tips.

The science of geology includes the specialist disciplines of petrology, palaeontology, mineralogy and crystallography — the studies of rocks, fossils, minerals and crystals. Palaeontology and stratigraphy help determine the relative age of rocks, placing them in the overall geological timescale. The principle of the latter is that the oldest rocks lie at the bottom of a succession, but in Cornwall this becomes far from simple where rocks have been folded, faulted or intruded with igneous rocks. Geomorphology is concerned with the processes involved in shaping landscape features.

This book introduces the subject to the visitor or resident who wishes to know more about the county, in the hope that it will stimulate further interest. After giving an outline geological history, the formation and properties of the main rock types are described, followed by the more common minerals and some rarer types. The importance of physical geology is stressed, for the underlying rocks and their structures have influenced the formation of many features in the inland and coastal landscapes. Brief mention is also made of economic geology: the commercial exploitation of Cornwall's rocks and minerals. Finally, a gazetteer describes sites chosen for their geological interest around the county. A Further Reading section suggests titles for more detailed research.

GEOLOGICAL HISTORY OF CORNWALL

Geological processes have been active throughout time, with major changes brought about by mountain-building phases (orogenies) which were accompanied by volcanic or other igneous activity and the folding, faulting and alteration (metamorphism) of existing rocks. The land which is now Cornwall has seen periods of uplift and sinking beneath the sea. It was during the latter that deposits were laid down, later to form the shales, slates and sandstones which make up most of the county. Climate changed too, for the land was once close to the Equator before continental drift began to take it northwards about 200 million years ago.

There are older rocks on the Lizard peninsula, but Cornwall consists mainly of Devonian rocks, known locally as 'killas', and Carboniferous-age Culm Measures in the north. There are some minor igneous intrusions around the county, but inland Cornwall is dominated by a spine of granite bosses, intruded during the

GEOLOGICAL TIMESCALE

ERA	PERIOD/EPOCH	TIME BEGUN (million years before present)
	QUATERNARY	
	Holocene (Recent)	0.01
	Pleistocene (Glacial)	3
	TERTIARY	
	Pliocene	12
CAENOZOIC	Miocene	25
	Oligocene	39
	Eocene	70
	Cretaceous	135
MESOZOIC	Jurassic	180
	Triassic	225
	Permian	280
	Carboniferous	350
PALAEOZOIC	Devonian	400
	Silurian	440
	Ordovician	500
	Cambrian	600
	PRE-CAMBRIAN	

Armorican or Variscan orogeny of the late Carboniferous and early Permian times. The majority of rocks were in place by the early Permian and the subsequent history has been one of denudation by erosion. Rocks of more recent age are lacking except for a few isolated deposits.

The geology of the metamorphic and igneous rocks of the appropriately named Lizard Complex is indeed complex and not fully understood. The oldest rocks of the Lizard peninsula may be Pre-Cambrian, but most have undergone subsequent metamorphism, and include the Old Lizard Head Series (slates, sandstones and volcanic rocks changed into mica-schists and quartzites) and more extensive hornblende-schists of Traboe and Landewednack types. The largest early igneous intrusion was that of a peridotite plug during an orogeny at the start of the Cambrian. This has since been mostly altered by metamorphism to the famous 'serpentine' rocks for which the Lizard is well known. Later igneous intrusions of gabbro, troctolite, basalt and micro-granites were intruded in mid-Devonian times. The Kennack gneiss is another important Lizard rock. Many of the rock types are in blocks separated by faults. During the Armorican orogeny, the northern edge of the complex was faulted against the younger Gramscatho Beds to the north, forming the Meneage Breccia which is exposed in the coast northwards from Porthallow.

The only Ordovician and Silurian rocks in Cornwall are quartzites and limestones found as broken masses in breccias. The Meneage Breccia consists of masses and broken fragments of identifiable Lizard rocks from the vicinity, as well as quartzites and limestones of the Ordovician and Silurian periods. These last can be matched with the contents of a similar zone of breccia to the north-east at Carne (Gerrans Bay) and between Veryan Bay and Gorran Haven, cutting off the phyllites of Dodman Head. Both districts contain Upper Devonian rocks, part of the Veryan Series.

The Caledonian orogeny of the late Silurian uplifted land to the north, but the site of Cornwall was then under the sea. During the

Devonian period, it took the form of a geosynclinal basin, or a subsiding downfold which continued to fill with material brought down by rivers from this northern landmass. Coarser material was deposited close to the old shore to form sandstones and gritstones, while the finer particles were carried further into the sea and deposited to form mudstones, shales and siltstones. Occasionally, limestones were formed where there was shallower water.

Most of Cornwall is therefore of this Devonian 'killas', sedimentary rocks in part or wholly changed into slates by subsequent pressure. The period has been divided into the Lower, Middle and Upper Devonian, within which numerous formations have been identified, each named after a type-site locality. However, it is difficult to determine the age and boundaries of some Devonian rocks, especially to the west (probably Middle Devonian) and the sequence is still by no means certain.

The Lower Devonian Dartmouth Beds are mainly argillaceous (clayey) and include shaly slates, siltstones and sandstones. Green and purple slates occur at Watergate Bay on the north coast and Talland Bay on the south. These are overlain by the Meadfoot Beds, which are successions of slates, siltstones and sandstones, and sometimes thin-bedded limestones, indicating shallow waters. There was volcanic activity during the Meadfoot phase, leaving coarse agglomerates and tuffs, exposed around St Austell Bay. The Staddon Grits of sandstones and thin limestones may follow the Meadfoot Beds, or be of the same age.

Middle Devonian rocks have been much folded and faulted since their formation. They include the Gramscatho Beds, interbedded greywackes and slates with some limestones, conglomerates, cherts and spilitic lavas. The slates and siltstones of the Mylor Beds are also believed to be Middle Devonian. Middle or Upper Devonian limestones contain corals, an indication of clear shallow water conditions in a warm climate. They occur mostly in south Devon but a small outcrop of the Plymouth limestone is exposed at Cremyll on the Cornish shore of the lower Tamar estuary.

The main Upper Devonian rocks are found in north Cornwall. There was large-scale volcanic activity around Pentire Head, where pillow lavas are some 200 ft [60 m] thick. Above lie the Merope Island Beds of dark grey slates, and then banded slates of purple and green. More important commercially, are the fine-grained grey slates which are found in the Upper Devonian rocks from Tintagel to Launceston, and are the source of the best Cornish slates, quarried extensively around Delabole and Tintagel. The Veryan Series of the Upper Devonian are found in south Cornwall, in a narrow belt from Mullion to Gorran Haven (see page 2). Where they were faulted against the Lizard Complex and Gramscatho Beds during the Armorican orogeny, there are breccias and conglomerates, interbedded with greywackes, slates and limestones.

The so-called 'Culm Measures' of the Carboniferous extend across north Cornwall and are exposed along the coast all the way from Boscastle to the Devon border and beyond. The Lower Carboniferous includes black shales, fine sandstones and some thin limestones. The Barras Nose Formation has shales, siltstones, thin sandstones and crinoidal limestones, exposed at Willapark and Tregardock.

Tuffs, agglomerates and spilitic lavas are evidence of widespread volcanic action in the Lower Carboniferous. Lavas are exposed in the cliffs around Tintagel and continue inland to the south-east towards Launceston, where, for example, they were used in part for building the castle. Also in this Launceston area are beds of chert in a series of ridges extending to the coast at Fire Beacon Point. These cherts may have formed in lagoons, and some contain traces of radiolaria, the silica skeletons of microscopic sea creatures.

All these rocks have been much folded and faulted, as have those of the Upper Carboniferous. Here, the Crackington Formation consists of shales and thin turbidite sandstones, and the Bude Formation has thick beds of sandstones with siltstones and shales.

It was the Armorican mountain-building orogeny which produced the very complex series of folds, overfolds and faults now seen in north Cornwall. The Lizard rocks were serpentinised at this time. The South-West peninsula became part of a much larger belt of fold mountains which included Brittany and South-West Ireland in late Carboniferous and early Permian times, about 280 million years ago, when granite was emplaced as a fairly fluid magma deep beneath these older rocks. It came from a common source, the so-called Cornubian batholith, and subsequent erosion of the cover rocks has exposed the five main granite bosses of Bodmin Moor, Hensbarrow (St Austell), Carnmenellis, Land's End (West Penwith) and the Isles of Scilly. The larger Dartmoor in Devon is part of the same system. Lesser intrusions are found at Tregonning Hill, Carn Brea and Carn Marth in the west, and Kit Hill and Hingston Down in the east, with much smaller exposures at St Michael's Mount, St Agnes Beacon, Cligga Head, St Dennis, Belowda Beacon and Castle-an-Dinas. At a late stage, some of the granites were altered in several ways, the most widespread being the formation of kaolinite or china clay. Minor acid rocks were intruded vertically into fissures as dykes and horizontally as sills. These include aplites, pegmatites, and the more extensive quartz-porphyry elvans. Mineralisation also occurred at a late stage during the cooling of the granite, with the intrusion of tin and copper in east-west lodes and lead, zinc and iron in north-south lodes.

The intense heat of the magma baked the rocks surrounding the granite intrusions (contact metamorphism), forming a ring of altered rocks known as the metamorphic aureole.

Most of the present Cornish rocks were in place by the end of the Carboniferous. From then on, the mountain chain was gradually worn down to its roots by the processes of weathering and erosion. This exposed the granite, but the whole land mass was meanwhile going through phases of uplift or drowning by advances of the sea. Although long since removed by erosion, Cornwall may have been covered with the same sedimentary Cretaceous rocks which dominate the geology of south and south-east England today.

The county's youngest geology dates from the Late Tertiary and Quaternary. A Mio-Pliocene high level erosion platform has been recognised at around 1,000 ft [300 m] on Bodmin Moor. This may not be of marine origin, but certainly lower platforms have been shown to be so. A Pliocene platform at about 430 ft [130 m] is clearly seen at several places, but especially on the Lizard peninsula and between Redruth and St Agnes. Related deposits of marine sands and clays occur on Crousa Downs (Lizard), around St Agnes Beacon and on Polcrebo Downs to the south of Camborne. Sands and clays at St Erth are considered to be Pliocene or Pleistocene by different researchers.

Pleistocene geology is related to glaciation, which caused sea level to fall about 300 ft [90 m] lower than today. There were cycles of cold phases with perhaps six main glaciations, each lasting several thousand years and separated by temperate periods or interglacials. The greatest glaciation was the Wolstonian, when Irish Sea ice lay just off the north coast, with some possibly passing over the Isles of Scilly, where glacial material has been identified on the north end of St Martin's, Tresco and Bryher. Glacial erratics are also found, by far the largest being the Giant's Rock near Porthleven. The rest of the land was frozen under periglacial conditions, with widespread permafrost. The main Pleistocene deposits are of 'head', an ill-sorted mass of rock debris which was moved downslope in these conditions by a process known as solifluction. Head occurs in valleys but is best seen where it is exposed along the coast.

Much of the physical geology of the landscape is related to sea level changes, giving raised beaches and drowned valleys (rias) around the coast. The sea advanced across the land at different intervals, leaving a series of planed-off surfaces or platforms as noted above. These and raised beaches are evidence of subsequent falls in sea level. However, rises in the Flandrian or post-glacial period in the last 10,000 years have flooded the lower courses of river valleys forming 'rias' and submerged forests are also evidence. Today, the large dunes of blown sand along the north coast are perhaps the sedimentary rocks of the future.

ROCK TYPES

Rocks are classified as three types, according to their mode of formation: igneous, metamorphic and sedimentary. Colour, texture grain size and mineral constituents all help identify them. Where there is no exposure or outcrop, an examination of the material used in older buildings and stone hedges will often give a clue to the local rock types.

IGNEOUS ROCKS

These are rocks formed from molten magma. They may be intrusive rocks, formed beneath cover rocks, as for example granites or gabbros. Major deep-seated intrusions are known as batholiths, from which may emerge bosses. These 'plutonic' rocks are generally coarser-grained because their slow cooling allowed large crystals to grow. Minor intrusions exploited and filled fissures or planes of weakness, forming sills and dykes. The former are horizontal sheets which can be exposed as a steep escarpment, where large enough. The

Bodmin Moor granite (De Lank). *P.S.*

Carnmenellis granite (Bosahan). *P.S.*

latter are vertical or near-vertical sheets and can be seen cutting across other rock types and structures. They may be emphasised further where the rocks have different resistances to weathering. These rocks may be medium-grained and include dolerites or 'greenstones'.

Extrusive or volcanic rocks are usually lavas which have flowed out onto the land surface before solidifying. They tend to be fine-grained, as they cooled more rapidly. Where extruded beneath the sea they form pillow lavas. Other volcanic rocks are pyroclastics, containing fragments of lava and other rock thrown out during an eruption.

The rate of cooling affected the size of grains. Crystals had longer to form with the slow-cooling granites, contrasting with lavas which may be glassy in the case of obsidian. A rock is fine-grained if the average grain size is less than 0.1 mm, medium-grained 0.1 to 1–2 mm, and coarse-grained over 1–2 mm. In a porphyritic texture, the ground mass may contain larger crystals (phenocrysts) in which case it is known as a pegmatite.

Most igneous rocks contain quartz, feldspar, pyroxene, olivine, mica and hornblende, with minor accessory minerals. Free quartz crystals are formed from an excess of silica in the magma and the greater the content, the more acid is the rock (over c.66% silica). These are lighter coloured, such as coarse-grained granites and fine-grained rhyolite. The more basic rocks (45-55% silica) such as gabbro, dolerite (diabase) and basalt tend to be dark. Ultra-basic rocks (with less than c.45% silica) include peridotite.

AGGLOMERATE is of volcanic origin, a mixture of broken fragments of new or old rock within a finer matrix of volcanic ash. It may also include 'bombs' thrown out from a nearby volcano.

APLITE occurs in veins and may be associated with pegmatite. It is a pale grey quartz-feldspar rock formed at a late stage of the consolidation of the granite magma. Fine-grained veins can be seen cutting through the granite in certain quarries.

DOLERITE contains dark brown or greenish augite with some feldspar. When metamorphosed, it may be termed diabase.

ELVAN is a term used by quarrymen and miners to cover the micro-granite dykes which traverse the county parallel to the main ENE to WSW mineral lodes, cutting through the granites and surrounding country rocks. True elvan is a QUARTZ-PORPHYRY, which has a very fine ground mass with dominant quartz and feldspar phenocrysts. FELSITE is a non-porphyritic variety, with very fine grains. Some elvans are suitable as a building stone, such as at Newham which can be seen in houses in Lemon Street, Truro. The PENTEWAN STONE was quarried near St Austell and used in medieval churches and more recently in Antony House near Torpoint. 'Blue elvan' is a confusing term applied by quarrymen to greenstones when worked for roadstone.

GABBRO is a coarse-grained basic rock, containing dark augite and plagioclase (feldspar). Pale green olivine indicates a deficiency of free quartz, although some quartz may be present. There are other accessory minerals. Gabbro may have a banded structure. The grey-green Lizard gabbro has been metamorphosed, but unaltered black gabbro does occur.

GRANITE is the most readily recognised of the Cornish rocks, but there is an amazing variation between and within granite districts. It can be inspected where it outcrops or has been quarried, and in many buildings or tombstones throughout the county. It is grey when weathered and covered with lichen, but freshly broken granite reveals a crystalline mass of white or glassy grey quartz, white orthoclase feldspar and shiny black (biotite) or white (muscovite) micas. Polished granite shows the crystals to great effect. The formation and final sizes of the crystals were related to the rate of cooling and the composition of the original magma. Most granites are coarse-grained, and extremely long feldspars (phenocrysts) can be seen in a finer groundmass at Lamorna or Luxulyan in the Land's End and Hensbarrow districts. Bodmin Moor and Carnmenellis are noted for medium-grained granites. Some granites show an alignment of crystals in the direction of the flow of the magma before it

Gabbro dykes in serpentine.   *British Geological Survey*

cooled. Rarely, the crystals may form a cross. The feldspars are mostly white but can be pink or orangish-brown. Other constituent minerals include black tourmaline. Xenoliths are patches of darker material derived from the country rocks into which the granite was intruded. Sometimes, there are areas of fine-grained granite, such as that revealed at Castle-an-Dinas quarry near Penzance. Micro-granites occur at the chilled margins of granite intrusions or as lesser dykes or sills. Small exposures of pink granites are also found on the Lizard peninsula.

During a late stage of cooling, the granite magma gave off active solutions and volatile gases including fluorine, boron, sulphur dioxide and superheated steam. These entered fissures in the consolidated granite and gave rise to mineral lodes. Another hydrothermal process affected some parts of the granite, whereby the feldspars were broken down to KAOLIN (CHINA CLAY). There is evidence for this *kaolinisation* in all the granite districts, although the Hensbarrow granite was the most severely affected. CHINA STONE is a partially kaolinised granite enriched in fluorite and found in the Hensbarrow and Tregonning districts. Kaolinised rocks can be very weak and are a reminder that under certain conditions the apparently indestructible granite is just as vulnerable to decay as any other rock.

By *tourmalinisation*, mica was replaced by black boron-rich tourmaline, and eventually the feldspars were also replaced to form a quartz-schorl. Roche Rock is the best example, but there are other quartz-schorl dykes at the Devil's Jump and Lanlavery Rock on Bodmin Moor. LUXULLIANITE is a rare form of tourmalinised granite containing large crystals of pink feldspar set in a blue-black groundmass of quartz and schorl. Fluorine-rich vapours caused *greisening*, where feldspars were replaced by quartz and muscovite. There are good exposures of this in the small granite outcrops at Cligga Head and St Michael's Mount.

GREENSTONE is a term applied to many igneous intrusive rocks, often found as dykes and sills. Most are dolerite, but some basalt, andesite, proterobase and picrite are also included. Greenstone makes a good roadstone and has been quarried at several localities, most extensively at Penlee Quarry between Newlyn and Mousehole. It has formed resistant headlands, such as Black Head in St Austell Bay, and Gurnard's Head, Trevose Head, Stepper Point and The Rumps on the north coast. CATACLEWS STONE is a dark, blue-grey variety of greenstone found in a proterobase sill at Cataclews Point between Harlyn and Mother Ivey's Bays. Capable of being carved and polished, it was exploited in the medieval period, as can be seen to advantage in the pillars and font in nearby St Merryn church, or in Padstow church.

PEGMATITE is very coarsely crystalline, occurring mainly as dykes or sills in the granite margins, or the surrounding country rocks such as in the cliffs east of Trewavas Head (Tregonning granite). Pegmatites may include beryl, tourmaline, lithia micas and metallic minerals of economic importance.

PERIDOTITE is a dull green to black, ultra-basic rock, containing olivine, pyroxene and/or hornblende. It is found on the Lizard peninsula, but most has been altered to serpentinite.

PICRITE is another ultra-basic rock, of which a serpentinised example is POLYPHANT STONE, found near that hamlet to the south-west of Launceston. It has an attractive greenish colour with brown flecks when cut, and being soft when freshly quarried, it was therefore once in demand for carved church fittings etc. Another serpentinised picrite occurs at Clicker Tor, Menheniot, where it has been quarried for roadstone and railway ballast.

PILLOW LAVA was formed when volcanoes erupted beneath the sea in Middle and Upper Devonian times. The molten lava consolidated in pillowy forms as it rolled forwards and cooled. As with other types, it is a vesicular lava, the rock containing vesicles or cavities of gas and steam bubbles. The best place to see pillow lava is along the coast at Pentire Head.

TROCTOLITE is a rock of the Lizard peninsula, occurring as veins and dykes in the serpentinite, for example at Coverack. It contains plagioclase and olivine, and is distinguished by spots of red serpentine.

TUFF is a consolidated volcanic ash, usually deposited in layers.

Pillow lava, Pentire.   *British Geological Survey*

METAMORPHIC ROCKS

These are rocks which have been changed at depth by heat, pressure or both agents. New textures, minerals or rocks may be formed, determined by the extent of metamorphism and the nature of the original rock. For example, limestone was altered to marble, sandstone to quartzite, shale and mudstone to slate or schist. There are low, medium and high grades of metamorphism. High-grade regional metamorphism may alter both sedimentary and igneous rocks to form a gneiss. Lineation of crystals is common in most metamorphic rocks, showing cleavage or foliation.

Regional metamorphism refers to a large area of rocks subjected to heat and pressure during a mountain-building period. Thermal or contact metamorphism concerns only the rocks immediately adjacent to an igneous intrusion, where they have been intensely altered and recrystallised by local heating. The area of baked country rocks around the Cornish granites is known as a metamorphic aureole.

The most common rocks include slate, a fine-grained rock with cleavage planes where platy minerals lie at right angles to the maximum pressure. Phyllite is coarser than slate. Medium regional metamorphism may create coarse-grained schists, characterised by layering defined by elongated minerals, for example mica-schists which show wavy lines of platy micas.

CALC-FLINTA is a hard whitish stone which has been altered by contact metamorphism from calcareous rocks rich in silica. It is found in the metamorphic aureole of Bodmin Moor at Advent and Pantersbridge, and in a long arc around the north of the Hensbarrow granite from Lostwithiel to St Columb Major.

GNEISS results from high temperature and pressure. On the Lizard, the Kennack gneiss has pale bands of a coarser quartz and feldspar rock alternating with dark bands of a fine-grained basic rock of mainly hornblende. It appears to have been originally an igneous rock, possibly granite, intruded in dykes and sills into the gabbro and serpentinite.

HORNFELS is a hard, dark brown or green product of contact metamorphism. It occurs in the metamorphic aureole of the Land's End granite, where the greenstones and slates were subjected to great heat. On the north side of the granite, the greenstone-hornfels at Botallack and Kenidjack have a complex mineralogy.

PHYLLITE is slightly coarser and not as strong as slate but has undergone a greater metamorphism. It has a silver-grey sheen due to muscovite and chlorite flakes, and splits along cleavage planes. It is found in the north around Tintagel and in the south at the Dodman Head.

QUARTZITE is a quartz-grained sandstone which has been cemented hard by pressure or heat. Blocks of Ordovician quartzite are found on the coast at Carne, Gorran Haven and Porthallow.

SCHIST is the result of intense pressure and heat on sedimentary rocks. Brownish mica-schists have a wavy foliation, with silvery layers on account of the mica content. Hornblende-schists have a high hornblende content. Such rocks are found on the Lizard peninsula. In north Cornwall, a micaceous schist occurs in the metamorphic aureole between Camelford and Davidstow Moor, and pillow lavas near Tintagel have been altered to green schists.

SERPENTINITE, more commonly called serpentine, is the famous rock of the Lizard peninsula. It was originally an ultra-basic peridotite, but metamorphism altered the main constituent olivine into the mineral serpentine. The rock is banded and streaked with pale veins, and polishing shows up the contrasting dark greens and reds. There are three types: the finer tremolite- and dunite-serpentinites, and the coarser bastite-serpentinite near the centre of the exposure.

SLATE was formed from sedimentary mudstones or shales under pressure (regional metamorphism). Cleavage planes lie at right angles to the direction of pressure and do not relate to the original bedding. The best commercial slates split evenly and very thinly along these lines. Hard grey Devonian slates of good quality have been quarried for centuries at Delabole, around Tintagel and at St Neot. Elsewhere, with a few exceptions, the slates are rather poor, being soft, sandy or shaly. They may be crossed with veins of quartz. Slates vary in colour from dark to light grey, green, purple and brown. So-called 'rustic' slates are stained by iron, and are in demand as a building and decorative stone. SPOTTED SLATES result from contact metamorphism next to the granite, with high temperature minerals forming round spots. These become pale when the rock weathers.

SEDIMENTARY ROCKS

Such rocks were laid down as a sediment, usually beneath the sea. Detrital or clastic rocks contain broken down particles of eroded rocks, and their textures include rudaceous (coarse) pebbles, arenaceous (medium-textured) sand and sandstone, and argillaceous (fine) clay, shale and mudstone. Non-clastic rocks are mainly of chemical or biological origin. Cornish examples include calcareous rocks, such as limestones which may be chemically formed or contain shell fragments, and siliceous rocks such as flint and chert. Fossils of sea creatures occur in sedimentary rocks, although Cornish examples are seldom spectacular.

BRECCIA consists of angular rock fragments of many sizes and types in a matrix of smaller pieces. It may be the consolidated material resulting from the crushing of rocks by faulting, or scree material. The Meneage Breccia of the Lizard is the best known example.

CHERT is normally associated with limestone. It is similar to flint and occurs as beach pebbles on Loe Bar, derived from some offshore source. Silica-rich beds of radiolarian chert have minute skeletal remains of sea-dwelling radiolaria, and are found mainly between Launceston and Fire Beacon Point on the north coast.

CONGLOMERATE is a very coarse rock, consisting of a cemented mass of rounded pebbles of a variety of rock types. The toughest may be cemented by silica or oxides of iron or manganese. It is a feature found at the base of raised beaches.

FLINT is found as nodules in the Cretaceous chalk of southern England, which does not occur in Cornwall. However, it can be common as beach pebbles, most notably at Loe Bar near Porthleven. The very high flint content of the bar must represent the remains of cover rocks of chalk, or is derived from an outcrop on the floor of the English Channel. Flint contains pure silica and is shiny black when not discoloured. It has a distinct conchoidal or shell-shaped fracture when struck.

GRITSTONE is coarser than sandstone, with less well-rounded particles laid down as deltaic or shallow water deposits. Grey or reddish brown gritstones are found in the Devonian Grampound Grits of mid-Cornwall and in the Carboniferous 'Culm Measures' of the north.

LIMESTONE occurs in Cornwall mainly as thin beds alternating with other sedimentaries. Where formed from fragments of shells or skeletal material, its presence may be an indication of shallower waters. Occasionally, beds are thick enough to have been quarried, such as a Carboniferous limestone at Cannapark to the west of Launceston, a stone which yielded several fossils. A most distinct Middle Devonian limestone, grey with reddish veins and a high coral content, can be examined in a small exposure on the Cornish shore at Cremyll. However, this rock is far more abundant in the cliffs along the Hoe at Plymouth. It was extensively quarried around Plymouth and some was shipped coastwise for burning in limekilns at many small creeks and ports. This 'imported' limestone was also used for building, as at Looe where it can be seen in the church and some buildings upstream at Sandplace, where there are several disused limekilns. Blocks of Ordovician and Silurian limestones occur in the breccias of the Veryan Series.

SANDSTONE of marine origin has mainly rounded quartz particles which have been cemented together, perhaps by silica. Exposed strata may show ripple marks. Turbidite sandstones formed where the sediments were disturbed by turbidity or sea-floor currents descending the slopes of geosynclinal basins. They may be poorly sorted or show graded bedding, with coarser sandstone at the base becoming a fine siltstone at the top of each bed. Greywacke is another term for this type of sandstone.

SHALE is formed from clays and mudstones. It is fine-grained and splits easily with all the appearances of slate except that it is much softer and weaker. Where found in beds between sandstones or limestones, it indicates changing conditions of deposition.

Sand blocks at Godrevy.   *P.S.*

PLIOCENE, PLEISTOCENE AND RECENT DEPOSITS

Surface geology includes mostly unconsolidated deposits such as clays, sands, head, alluvium and peat.

ALLUVIUM refers to the finer particles deposited by the action of rivers, and is widespread especially in the lower courses of river valleys. It often contains minerals such as cassiterite and perhaps even gold in small quantities. These alluvial deposits have completely blocked the upper tidal reaches of the Fal and some of its tributaries, this being aided by the addition of mining waste thrown into the rivers over the centuries.

CLAY deposits are found, for example, at St Erth and around St Agnes Beacon. These are believed to be of Pliocene age and of marine origin. Kaolin or china clay is not of sedimentary origin.

HEAD is earthy with a mass of angular rock fragments and was transported by solifluction during periglacial conditions. Most deposits date from the last, Devensian, glaciation of the Pleistocene. It infills valley bottoms to as much as a depth of 100 ft [30 m] deep, but is best seen where it is exposed along the coast.

PEAT formed during the post-glacial period

especially on the granite upland of Bodmin Moor, where it covers alluvium as valley bogs and is found as blanket bogs on the hills between. This is geology in the making, but it is also significant on that peat hides the solid geology beneath.

SAND beds are unconsolidated, and those at St Erth and St Agnes are perhaps of Pliocene age. The former were once dug as moulding sand for the Harvey's foundry at Hayle. Coarser sands and gravels of a similar date occur at Polcrebo Downs near Crowan and Crousa Downs near Coverack.

BLOWN SAND is found mainly on the north coast at Sennen, Hayle, Gwithian, Perranporth, Holywell Bay, Crantock, Newquay, Constantine and Daymer Bay, with smaller examples on the south coast at Marazion, Praa Sands and Gunwalloe. Shell sand is light and easily blown by the wind, and has formed dunes over 200 ft [60 m] high at Hayle (Upton Towans) and Perranporth (Penhale Sands). Churches and settlements have been buried by the advance of the sand, such as St Gothian's chapel at Gwithian, St Piran's oratory and a settlement at Penhale Sands, St Constantine's chapel at Constantine, and St Enodoc church at Daymer Bay.

'BEACH ROCK' occurs in places, where the shelly sand has becomes cemented together to form a rock, as seen at Godrevy, Newquay, Mother Ivey's Bay, Harlyn Bay and Bude. It hardens with exposure and has been used by church-builders at Crantock and Padstow.

FOSSILS

Cornish geology is not noted for well-preserved fossils, although they do occur in the sedimentary and metamorphic rocks. These are fossils of sea-dwelling creatures such as ammonites, brachiopods, goniatites, trilobites, corals, crinoids (sea-lilies) and even fish. Usually, the resistant parts have been preserved; they may have been pyritised or their form may survive as moulds or casts. They

Cyrtospirifer extensus, from upper Devonian slate, Delabole Quarry.

Fossil found at Lanterdan quarry.   P.S.

provide the only evidence of life in the Devonian and Carboniferous seas of Cornwall. There are also some plant remains in the Carboniferous Culm Measures.

Because some creatures evolved relatively quickly over time, their fossils are important for dating rocks or providing a correlation with others in the area. Trilobites are useful for dating, such as the trilobite *basilicus tyrannus* from Veryan, while the ammonite *clymenia* species from South Petherwin is only found in Devonian rocks. Certain fossils, including brachiopods, trilobites and corals, have helped date the few Ordovician and Silurian rocks present in Cornwall.

While found in shales, sandstones and even slates, fossils are more common in the few exposures of limestone. For example, over 70 species are known from six limestone beds at South Petherwin. Devonian corals can be recognised, such as *Pachypora cervicornis* from Lower Devonian rocks at Polruan near Fowey. Other corals include *Petraia celtica* from Looe, Padstow and St Columb Porth.

The fish *Pteraspis cornubica* has been found in Lower Devonian rocks at Polperro, and its scales and spines at Lantivet and Watergate Bays. Other fish remains are known, for example, at Portwrinkle and Bude, the latter being in Upper carboniferous shales.

The most distinctive of the fossils found in the slates is the Delabole 'Butterfly', actually the much-flattened brachiopod *Cyrtospirifer verneuili*. This is from the type-site at Delabole Quarry, in Upper Devonian slates.

The more recent St Erth Beds (Pliocene or Pleistocene) have yielded a good collection of fossils, including oysters.

MINERALS

Many rocks contain the rock-forming minerals such as quartz, feldspar, augite, hornblende and olivine, but ore minerals are of the greatest interest in a county like Cornwall.

Mineral ore bodies are limited in their extent, and were formed during the late cooling of the granite magmas, when gases were forced into fissures or faults in the granite and surrounding rocks of the metamorphic aureole. These solidified into veins or lodes of varying width and length. The main lodes are aligned WSW to ENE, tending towards west–east in east Cornwall. They are usually vertical or steeply dipping, although the Great Flat Lode south of Carn Brea has an average dip of only 40°. Caunter lodes dip in the reverse direction to normal lodes, while cross-course lodes are at right angles and may even displace the main lodes. Stockworks consist of a mass of veinlets, and examples were worked opencast at Mulberry and Wheal Prosper near Lanivet. Other ore bodies include rich localised replacement structures known as carbonas, which were a feature of mines in the St Ives district.

Secondary enrichment is a result of chemical weathering along the outcrop of the lode. Copper may be leached out and pass in solution down to the zone of secondary enrichment to be deposited in the lode as carbonates and oxides above the water table and sulphides below. The gossan remains at the surface, a mass of mainly unleached iron compounds and a good indicator to mining prospectors of possible riches beneath.

There is a certain zoning of minerals, with those formed at the highest temperatures being nearest the granite. Hypothermal ores (formed at 300–500°C) include cassiterite, wolframite, arsenopyrite, molybdenite, sphalerite and chalcopyrite, the mesothermal ores (200–300°C) uranium, cobalt and bismuth, and the epithermal ores (50–200°C) lead, zinc, silver, iron and antimony. These last tend to be found in north–south cross-courses.

The main copper and tin lodes and mining districts are around St Just, St Ives, Camborne–Redruth, Wendron, St Day–Gwennap, St Agnes–Perranporth, St Austell, Liskeard and Callington–Gunnislake. Lead, zinc and iron lodes tend to be outside the usual mineral districts, being mined at places such as West Chiverton and East Wheal Rose, the Great Perran Iron Lode, Restormel Royal Iron Mine and the lead districts of Herodsfoot and Menheniot. Many other minerals have been exploited in the past, such as manganese at Treburland near Altarnun, or antimony which was mined on remote clifftop sites between Pentire and Port Quin, and to the south of Port Isaac. Uranium (Pitchblende) was mined at Wheal Trenwith at St Ives, and South Terras to the west of St Austell. Small quantities of bismuth, cobalt and nickel have been recovered, mostly from East Pool Mine, and molybdenum in the Kit Hill–Hingston Down district.

Silver is usually associated with lead, and was important at West Chiverton, East Wheal Rose

The Zone of Secondary Enrichment

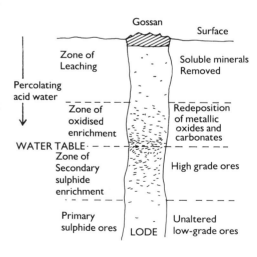

and mines at Menheniot and Callington. Gold occurs in the gossans, but mostly in alluvial deposits where it has been found during tin streaming. Gold from Carnon and Ladock is displayed in the Royal Cornwall Museum, but traces have been known from many other sources.

Lodes also contain gangue minerals alongside the metalliferous minerals. These include quartz, feldspar, muscovite, tourmaline and fluorite, which miners have often considered as waste or of little value. Nevertheless, they are a very important part of Cornwall's geology.

Alluvial deposits containing tin ores occur in many Cornish valley gravels. The lode outcrops were eroded by rivers back in Miocene or Pliocene times, and the ore material was transported and deposited in valley bottoms. During milder spells towards the close of the Pleistocene, violent melt-waters sorted this out by carrying away the lighter gravel and leaving the much heavier tin stones behind in beds. These were later covered by lighter alluvium as the floods subsided, to be discovered by the early tin streamers. Smaller particles of tin may also be found on some beaches.

All minerals require a cavity such as a vugh for the growth of true crystal forms. More often, minerals have formed as a crystalline mass, making identification more difficult. A good handbook is essential for the identification of minerals, but some optical and physical characteristics of help include:

Crystal form, of which there are seven crystal systems or families. For example, the cubic system includes galena, pyrite and blende. Cassiterite and chalcopyrite are tetragonal. Quartz, calcite and tourmaline are trigonal, orthoclase feldspar is monoclinic, and plagioclase feldspar is triclinic. These form under perfect conditions, but they are more commonly modified or found in a massive crystalline form (except in museums!!). Sometimes two crystals may be seen to be twinned. Crystallography is a complex subject.

Habit or form refers to characteristics such as crystal shape. The more distinct and readily recognisable types include acicular or needle-like (tourmaline), botryoidal, mamillated or rounded (haematite), foliated (muscovite), or bladed (wolframite).

Lustre of a fresh specimen includes metallic (such as iron pyrites), sub-metallic (wolframite),

vitreous or glassy (quartz), resinous (zinc blende) pearly (talc or muscovite) and adamantine, as of diamonds (cassiterite). Weathered minerals, such as galena, may be dull with no lustre.

Colour is important but can vary considerably such as in quartz which may be clear, milky white, pink, smoky, etc. Copper minerals may be a distinctive green (malachite) or blue (azurite). The yellowish copper pyrites or chalcopyrite can be identified from iron pyrites in that the latter is paler and more brassy.

Streak is more consistent than colour. A specimen can be rubbed on unglazed porcelain, or scratched by a penknife blade if possible. For example, fluorspar gives a white streak whatever its colour. Copper and iron pyrites both give a greenish-grey streak, but the former can be scratched more easily than the latter. Two dark minerals give surprising streaks: cassiterite is nearly white, while wolframite is chocolate brown.

Hardness is a helpful guide. The standard measure is known as Mohs' Scale of Hardness, increasing from the softest (1) to the hardest (10) so that each can be scratched by the next.

MOHS' SCALE OF HARDNESS

Hardness	
1	Talc
	crushed with finger nail
2	Gypsum
	scratched with fingernail
3	Calcite
	scratches with copper coin
4	Fluorite
5	Apatite
	scratches with penknife blade
6	Feldspar
	scratches with quartz
7	Quartz
	scratches window glass
	scratches with special steel file
8	Topaz
9	Corundum
10	Diamond

Specific gravity, or the relative density of a mineral is difficult to measure in the field, but just by weighing a suspect specimen in the hand is a good first indication that it might be mineralised. Most common minerals are in the range 2 – 7, but cassiterite or galena are heavy, at 7 and 7.6.

Cleavage is related to structure within the mineral. The micas have a perfect cleavage, flaking along definite planes. Fracture is irregular. Quartz has a uniform structure which gives a shell-like or conchoidal fracture, a type best seen in flint.

Some of the commoner Cornish minerals are listed below.

GANGUE AND ROCK-FORMING MINERALS

AUGITE, $(Ca,Mg,Fe,Al)_2(Al,Si)_2O_6$
A rock-forming silicate mineral of complex composition, found in gabbro, basalt and other igneous rocks. Greenish black, vitreous lustre.

BARYTES (HEAVY SPAR), $BaSO_4$.
Barium sulphate, heavier than fluorite. Colourless or white, but also yellow, brown or red. White streak. Perfect parallel cleavage. Associated with lead and zinc, and fluorspar and quartz, for example at Menheniot. Specific gravity 4.5.

CALCITE, $CaCO_3$.
Colourless or white when pure. Can be massive. Distinguished from quartz by hardness of 3. Hexagonal system, prismatic crystals. Cleavage is perfect parallel. Less common in Cornwall.

FELDSPAR, $KAlSi_3O_8$
Important rock-forming mineral, found in most igneous rocks. ORTHOCLASE, $KAlSi_3O_8$, is a potassium aluminium silicate. Best seen in the granites, where its crystals can be very long. Crystals exhibit simple Carlsbad twinning, their length being seen to be divided by a vitreous or dull lustre according to the angle of viewing. Hardness 6. PLAGIOCLASE may be rich in sodium (Na) or calcium (Ca).

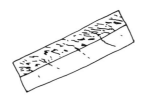

Orthoclase feldspar, showing Carlsbad twinning.

FLUORITE (FLUORSPAR), CaF_2
Associated with lead mining areas, but also elsewhere. Colour may be white, pink or green, but with white streak. Vitreous lustre. Distinguished by cubic forms. Hardness 4.

HORNBLENDE,
$(Ca,Mg,Fe,Na,Al)_{7-8}(Al,Si)_8O_{22}(OH)_2$

A complex silicate, found in igneous rocks such as diorite or gabbro, and in metamorphic rocks such as hornblende-schist. Green to black coloured crystals, prismatic or massive.

KAOLINITE, $Al_4Si_4O_{10}(OH)_8$
A clay mineral, usually known as china clay or kaolin. Formed from the alteration of feldspars in granite, most widespread by deep hydro-thermal activity but locally by weathering of exposed granite or within lodes.

MICA (BIOTITE), $K(Mg,Fe)_3AlSiO_{10}(OH,F)_2$
Black to brown colour, but with a pale or white streak. Easily recognised by shiny, thin flakes with perfect basal cleavage. Found in most granites.

MICA (MUSCOVITE), $KAl_2(AlSi_3O_{10})(OH,F)_2$
Pearly lustre, white streak and perfect basal cleavage. Occurs especially in granites, but also seen in some slates, sandstones and schists.

OLIVINE, $(Mg,Fe)_2SiO_4$
A pale green rock-forming mineral present in basic igneous rocks such as gabbro, troctolite and peridotite. It alters to serpentine.

QUARTZ, SiO_2
May be crystalline but more commonly in a

Quartz, hexagonal prism.

massive form. Hardness 7. Colourless or white when pure, but forms include pinks or even black. Vitreous lustre. A key ingredient of granite, but found in a great many rocks, often in veins.

SERPENTINE, $Mg_6[SiO_{10}](OH)_8$
Hydrous magnesium silicate. Massive form, green, red or brown colours, with veins of steatite. Hardness 3 to 4.

STEATITE (TALC), $Mg_3[SiO_{10}](OH)_2$
Colour white or shades of greenish-grey. Very soft (Hardness 1) with a greasy feel which gives it another name, Soapstone.

Tourmaline.

TOURMALINE,
$Na(Mg,Fe,Al,Mn)_3Al_6(BO_3)_3Si_6O_{18}(OH,F)_4$

Complex chemical composition. Tourmaline is an important accessory mineral in granite, found in characteristic black needle-like crystals. Where found in a vein or exposed sheet it is known as schorl.

ORE MINERALS

ARSENOPYRITE (MISPICKLE), FeAsS
Arsenical pyrites contains 46% arsenic. It has a metallic lustre, is tin-white in colour, tarnishing to grey-copper. It gives off a garlic smell when struck with steel. Hardness 5 to 5.6. Found in association with tin and copper lodes. Calcining of tin ores was necessary to remove this impurity, which later became a product in its own right.

AZURITE, $Cu_3(CO_3)(OH)_2$
Blue carbonate of copper, taking its name from its deep azure-blue colour. Found in the mines around Redruth.

BORNITE (PEACOCK ORE), Cu_5FeS_4
Usually massive form. Reddish colour quickly tarnishes and becomes iridescent, giving it the name Peacock Ore.

BOURNONITE (WHEEL ORE), $CuPbSbS_3$
Also called Endellionite, as it was first found at St Endellion in Cornwall. Crystal form gives it the very appropriate name Wheel Ore.

CASSITERITE, SnO_2
Tin oxide. For such a well-known Cornish mineral, it is not easy to actually find a specimen! Blackish-brown with adamantine lustre, crystals belong to tetragonal system, but may be massive. Hardness 6 to 7, and noticeable weight (specific gravity is 6.8 to 7.1). Wood Tin is a rounded variety with a radiating fibrous structure.

CHALCOCITE (COPPER GLANCE), Cu_2S
Also called Redruthite, this is a rich ore containing 79.8% copper. It was formed in the zone of secondary enrichment by the alteration of primary copper sulphides. Usually massive. Black-lead grey colour with a similar streak.

CHALCOPYRITE (COPPER PYRITES), $CuFeS_2$
Similar but yellower than iron pyrites, but still with greenish grey streak. Not as hard (3.5 to 4), crumbling when scratched with a knife. Usually found in massive form. A common copper ore (34.5 % copper).

COPPER, NATIVE, Cu
Pure copper found in fissures, often in dendritic forms. A large specimen from Mullion is exhibited in the Camborne School of Mines Museum.

CUPRITE (RED COPPER ORE), CuO_2
Red oxide of copper, of obvious colour. Found in the oxidised zone of copper lodes.

GALENA, PbS
Lead sulphide, the main lead ore in Cornwall. Lead grey colour and streak, metallic lustre when fresh. Classic cubic forms or massive. Very heavy (specific gravity 7.4 to 7.6). Hardness 2.5. Frequently associated with silver, and mined as such at East Wheal Rose, West Chiverton and mines around Menheniot and Calstock.

HAEMATITE, Fe_2O_3
Found in a characteristic mamillated or kidney

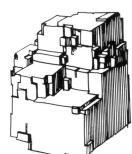

Galena.

shape, but fibrous internally. May have a metallic lustre, steel grey to black colour with a reddish coating. A very obvious cherry red streak. Hardness 5.5. to 6.5.

MALACHITE, $Cu_2CO_3(OH)_2$

Very distinct bright green colour when fresh. Surface is botryoidal or mamillated. Broken mineral shows a radiating fibrous form of silky lustre. Greenish-black streak. Hardness 3.5 to 4.

MOLYBDENITE, MoS_2

A lead-grey mineral with a metallic lustre, found in small veins or flakes in rock. Very soft, with a hardness of 1 to 1.5. Found on Kit Hill in small quantities.

PYRITE (IRON PYRITES), FeS_2

Pale brassy yellow colour when fresh with a metallic lustre, but with a greenish-grey streak. Hardness 6 to 6.5. It forms good cubic crystals, often marked with striations, but it is commonly massive.

SIDERITE (CHALYBITE), $FeCO_3$

Iron carbonate or spathose iron ore. Most commonly in a massive form. Pearly or vitreous lustre, pale yellow or buff to brownish-black where weathered, with a white streak.

WOLFRAMITE, $(Fe,Mn)WO_4$

Metallic, greyish black crystals easily recognised when in a bladed form. Distinct chocolate brown streak, and very heavy (specific gravity 7.1 to 7.9). Hardness 5 to 5.5. Found with tin, and once considered waste until used for hardening steel. Two mines which worked wolfram exclusively were Castle-an-Dinas, north of the Goss Moor, and Hawkswood near North Hill on Bodmin Moor.

ZINC BLENDE, ZnS

Also known as 'Black Jack'. Usually occurs in a massive form of brownish colour and resinous lustre. Less common are crystals of the tetrahedrite class of the cubic system. Hardness 3.5 to 4. Often associated with galena. A by-product to the more valuable tin at the Wheal Jane mine, in 1971–91.

RARE MINERALS AND GEMSTONES

Cornwall is noted for its rare minerals, many of which were first identified in the county's mines and can be seen in the collection at the Royal Cornwall Museum. Unusual names such as

bertranite, henwoodite, liskeardite, rashleighite, or russellite are just a few examples named after their localities or persons (not necessarily the discoverer). A single mine can yield a great variety of minerals in addition to the usual tin and copper ores. To give just one example, minerals obtained from the Phoenix United Mine on south-east Bodmin Moor include andrewsite, chalcosiderite, henwoodite, libethenite, tile ore (ziegelerz) and turquoise.

Semi-precious stones are mostly forms of silica. Glassy rock crystals of quartz were once known as 'Cornish diamonds'. Amethyst is purplish in colour, due to manganese. Chalcedony is related to flint, and varieties include the reddish-brown carnelian, the darker jasper, or the banded agate and onyx. Topaz occurs in pegmatites. Opal and pale blue turquoise are also known in Cornwall. Beaches are the best places for finding gemstones ready polished by wave action, especially at Marazion and Loe Bar. Garnets occur in metamorphic rocks such as hornfels, gneiss and schist, but are of little value as semi-precious stones.

Granite Tor Formation

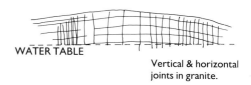

WATER TABLE

Vertical & horizontal joints in granite.

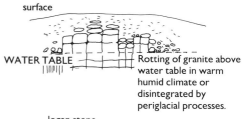

surface

WATER TABLE

Rotting of granite above water table in warm humid climate or disintegrated by periglacial processes.

logan stone

clitters

Tors exposed by removal of waste by solifluction. Clitters carried down-slope.

GEOLOGY AND STRUCTURE: FORMING THE LANDSCAPE

Many factors are involved in the formation of landscape features, both inland and coastal. They include rock types (their hardness, resistance to weathering and erosion, etc), sea level changes, river patterns and profiles, and climate. They are complex and often interrelated.

GRANITE LANDSCAPES

The characteristic upland granite landscape includes rounded hills, plateau tops, steep-sided valleys where rivers run off the moorland edge, marshy ground and rough vegetation. Rocky tors are found on some summits or spurs, but are by no means universal. Bodmin Moor has the best examples, and one of the most interesting areas to visit encompasses Stowe's Hill (Cheesewring), Sharp Tor, and the three parallel ridges of Bearah, Kilmar and Hawk's Tor. On the north moor, Roughtor exhibits all the typical features of granite tors, with a logan rock too.

There are three main joint systems which have greatly influenced the creation of granite landforms and rock features. Two sets of near-vertical joints at right angles to each other are the result of contraction as the granite magma cooled, while horizontal joints include 'pseudo-bedding planes' which may be pressure-release joints caused when the cover rocks were removed and the granite slopes roughed out by erosion. The joints of the tors can be seen closely following the shape of the summits at Roughtor and Stowe's Hill on Bodmin Moor. At the latter, they are also exposed in the main face of Cheesewring Quarry below.

Most tors exhibit a tabular nature, where they have been weathered out along the three main lines of joints. Closer joints expose a greater surface area to weathering processes, and thus the varying width between the joints has influenced the rate of weathering and erosion. The process of the formation of tors is controversial. Of the two main theories, one has it that the granite was first subjected to chemical weathering beneath the land surface when a warm humid climate prevailed, while

the other sees the cause to be frost action under periglacial (arctic) conditions in more recent years. However, both theories agree that the jointing controlled the extent of weathering and the final form of the tors, and importantly that the tors were finally revealed when the weathered material (growan) was removed downslope by solifluction during the Ice Ages. This mass movement of material carried with it the detached blocks which now lie scattered on the slopes surrounding their parent tors. Some of these clitters or moorstones show signs of splitting by frost action. Ever since, the exhumed tors have been subjected to the subaerial weathering agents of rain and wind.

Occasionally, a horizontal joint weathers out so far that a block becomes delicately poised, enabling it to be rocked or 'logged' with little effort, or even by the wind. The famous Logan Rock is at Treryn Dinas, near Land's End, but there are others in this district as well as on Bodmin Moor. The tops of some summit rocks are hollowed with rounded basins, where mildly acidic rainwater has weakened the feldspars so that the quartz grains become loosened. Such rock basins are found in all the main granite districts, as well as Carn Brea.

The broader effects of jointing and weathering on the granite landscape may be to create a 'basin and gorge' valley. The basins occur where there is kaolinisation or close jointing, while the gorge is where strong granite exists with widely-spaced joints. Between the valleys, the interfluves have corresponding cols and summits with tors or spreads of clitters. This has been described on Dartmoor, but is well seen with the Witheybrook valley on the east side of Bodmin Moor. The valley pattern is clearly related to the granite structure which trends WSW to ENE with a series of parallel ridges centred on Kilmar Tor (page 40).

FOLDING AND FAULTING

Sedimentary rocks were laid down under the sea in horizontal beds, each separated by clearly visible bedding planes. However, they are usually seen to have been tilted as a result

Types of folds

simple fold (anticline)   asymmetrical fold   overfold   recumbent overfold   overthrust fold (nappe)   thrust plane

of earth movements. The dip is the angle of slope of the bedding plane with the horizontal, and its direction is measured in relation to true north. The strike is the direction of any horizontal line drawn along the bedding plane. Folding and faulting are features of sedimentary and metamorphic rocks. Earth movements during the Armorican orogeny brought pressure from the south against an immovable block to the north, compressing the Cornish rocks which lay between into a series of folds with

Simple folding

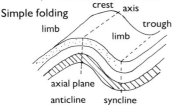

crest   axis   limb   trough   limb   axial plane   anticline   syncline

east–west trending axes. Some of the rocks are highly contorted, with strata so tilted to be standing vertically in places. These are features of the cliff face and there is little other resulting landform. The most dramatic examples are best seen in north Cornwall along the coast on either side of Bude, while folding, faulting and thrust planes are features of the Boscastle–Tintagel coast. Faults cross the county in north-west to south-east directions, for example from Boscastle to Portwrinkle or Rusey to the Tamar estuary. These formations are often extremely complex, but it is possible to recognise some basic forms.

The simplest fold is the anticline (upwards) or syncline (downwards) with symmetrical limbs. A feature where the axis (the central line through the crest of the fold) is also gently warped, is known as a pericline. The Whale Rock on the shore at Bude is a good example of this. The fold becomes asymmetrical with increased pressure from one direction, and this overfolding becomes more exaggerated with further pressure, forming a recumbent fold. Eventually, the rock may fracture so that the upper part of the fold is pushed bodily forward along a thrust plane to form a nappe.

Faults occur in many places, but are usually less

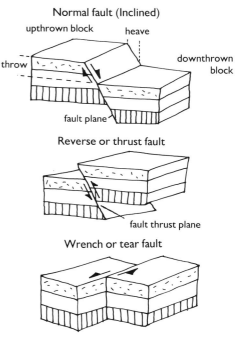

Normal fault (Inclined)

upthrown block   heave   downthrown block   throw   fault plane

Reverse or thrust fault

fault thrust plane

Wrench or tear fault

spectacular than the folding. A normal fault is vertical, or inclined as a result of tension. Compression, however, results in a reversed fault; if low-angled, it is a thrust fault. Horizontal displacement of rocks takes place along a tear or wrench fault.

EROSION SURFACES

Relative changes in sea level result from either movements of the sea (eustatic) or the land mass (isostatic). For example, an apparent fall in sea level may result from the widespread freezing of polar ice during an Ice Age, or the uplift of the land due to earth movements. The melting of the ice or sinking of the land has the reverse effect. The most obvious evidence for

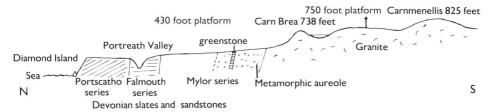

Cross-section between Diamond Island (Portreath) and Carmenellis, showing the 430 foot Pliocene marine platform and possible 750 foot platform.
(Note how the 430 foot platform is no respecter ot rock types.)

this can be seen in raised beaches close to the present shoreline, but there is a series of much higher erosion platforms.

The highest planation or erosion surface recognised in Cornwall is at 1,000 ft [300 m] above sea level on Bodmin Moor. It is most extensive on Davidstow Moor, but there are remnants elsewhere on the moor. At such a height this may be the result of Tertiary sub-aerial erosion rather than the work of the sea. There are later erosion surfaces at about 750 ft [230 m] and 630 ft [192 m], perhaps representing a late Tertiary transgression of the sea across the land. Successive retreats of the sea followed, pausing long enough to plane off the most convincing platform at around 430 ft [130 m]. This Pliocene platform is clearly seen across much of the Lizard peninsula and encircling the Land's End peninsula which would have been an island. Carn Brea and St Agnes Beacon still appear as two smaller islands standing up from the 430 ft platform along the north coast. Evidence that this is a marine-cut platform is shown in the way it has planed off all rock types including the granite at the foot of Carn Brea. The same platform lies at about 350 ft [106 m] at Tintagel, with old degraded cliffs rising behind. There are lower platforms at around 280 ft [85 m] and 100 ft [30 m]. Raised beaches are nearer present-day sea level, where actual beach material is exposed.

RIVERS

The ideal long profile of a river course is steep near its source, grading to a gentle slope as it approaches base level. Rapid erosion takes place near the headwaters, while deposition of alluvium occurs where the flow slows down near the sea. A relative fall in sea level (base

level) results in the rejuvenation of the lower course of a river, so that it begins cutting down vigorously to form a new graded profile. A knick point along a profile shows how far the rejuvenated river has cut back upstream. Downcutting may be held up by more resistant rock, such as where the Fowey meets granite at Golitha Falls. Different sea level changes may produce a series of knick points. Rocky Valley near Boscastle is a good example of a rejuvenated stream at work today, but all over Cornwall such action has formed incised valleys, which cut deeply into the general inland plateau surface. The meandering gorge of the Tamar between Greystone Bridge and Calstock is a classic example. Down-cutting would have been encouraged during the Pleistocene glaciations when sea level was perhaps 300 ft [90 m] lower and the valleys were scoured by meltwater floods.

Fowey River capture and drainage trends on Bodmin Moor and in South East Cornwall.

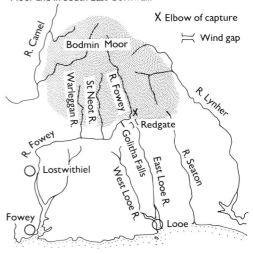

Drainage patterns may have been already established on older cover rocks, to be superimposed onto the present rocks as these were revealed by erosion. Uplift in the Mid-Tertiary gave a southerly tilt to the land mass, leading to the general trend seen today, with the main rivers of the Tamar, Lynher, Fowey and Fal draining to the south. This is most conspicuously in a NW to SE direction on Bodmin Moor, with rivers such as the Fowey, Witheybrook and Lynher. A radial drainage pattern appears to have been superimposed in the Carnmenellis district. The rivers here do not radiate from the highest point but from just to the north, which was presumably beneath the summit of a former dome of cover rocks.

River capture is seen where the rapidly downcutting headwaters of one stream literally 'capture' the waters of another. A classic example is the Fowey, which has taken the headwaters of the East Looe River near Golitha Falls, leaving a 'wind gap' or col just 40 ft [12 m] above the river at Redgate and an 'elbow of capture' at Draynes Bridge. The present East Looe River is now a 'misfit' stream, appearing far too small to have eroded the deep valley through which it flows. The River Camel may have flowed into the lower course of the Fowey before being captured by a stream cutting back from the north-west, leaving a less convincing wind gap between Bodmin and Lanhydrock.

PLEISTOCENE FEATURES

While Cornwall was never covered with glaciers during the Pleistocene, the landscape was barren and frozen hard under periglacial conditions. The formation of tors and dispersal of surface clitters around their slopes by solifluction has been described above. On the granite tors themselves and among their clitters, some rocks have been split by the expansion of water in cracks as it froze. For the best results, this freeze-thaw action requires the temperature to be changing constantly above and below freezing point between day and night. The mass movement process of solifluction took place during milder periods, when the upper part of the ground thawed enough for the earth and rock material

to slump downslope. This 'head' continued to flow down the valleys and was deposited to depths of up to 100 ft [30 m]. It is most commonly exposed in cliff sections where valleys meet the coast. Here it often overlies interglacial raised beaches.

Erratics are rocks which have been transported by glaciers or within icebergs and deposited far from their source. Often it is possible to identify the origin of the rock, and therefore the direction of ice flow, but the Giant's Rock (derived from a stranded iceberg) at Porthleven is still unidentified. Small erratics can be found in raised beach deposits, features which are described below.

COASTAL GEOLOGY AND SCENERY

The sea attacks the coast by several processes, forming cliffs, caves, arches, zawns, stacks and wave-cut platforms. Waves erode by hydraulic action, when they compress air trapped in fissures before it expands with explosive force. Corrasion (abrasion) occurs when sand and boulders are pounded against the foot of a cliff, undercutting it and forming a notch. They are also responsible for abrading wave-cut platforms. The boulders themselves are broken down by attrition. Corrosion (chemical weathering) is a feature of calcareous rocks such as limestone or chalk, but other rocks weather more rapidly in salt water. The rate of marine erosion is also affected by the size and fetch (distance travelled) of waves, and the amount of load they are carrying for abrasion.

Geology has affected the nature of coastal scenery, with factors such as differences in rock type, rock hardness, jointing, faults, mineral veins, bedding and the dip of rocks. Headlands and bays occur where there are alternating strong and weaker rocks, and the coast around

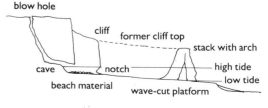

Wave-cut platform and other coastal features.

Newquay between Trevelgue Head and Ligger Point is just one of many examples.

The most impressive cliffs are seen along the Atlantic coasts of north Cornwall, Land's End and the west of the Lizard peninsula. Erosion in the far north is causing the weaker cliffs to retreat faster than some small streams can cut down, thus forming hanging valleys with waterfalls where they meet the sea. Higher Sharpnose Point and Tintagel Cove are among the best examples. Ideally, a notch might be expected to be cut by abrasion at the foot of the eroding cliff. A classic example can be seen near the Giant's Rock just west of Porthleven where the notch has been enlarged into caves in some places. In contrast, debris at the foot of a cliff or back of a beach gives protection against wave attack, so that some cliffs have been weathered back to a gentler angle and have become stabilized by vegetation. Some south coast cliffs, such as in Gerrans Bay, show little evidence of active erosion.

Bands of weak or heavily faulted rock may be exploited by hydraulic action to create blow-holes, caves and arches. Large caverns at Trevelgue Head near Newquay are well-

Caves and arches at Perranporth.

Porthleven, wave cut platform.   P.S.

known, while a much-photographed example of an arch is through the Enys Dodnan at Land's End. In some places there are funnels exposed on clifftops, where the roofs of deep caves have collapsed, as at the Lion's Den (Lizard), Devil's Frying Pan (Cadgwith) and two Round Holes at Trevone and Trevose Head. The existence of some huge caves and arches is unsuspected from the clifftop, and they can only be reached by small boat or canoe.

Zawns are common features along the Land's End granite coast, although they are found in other rocks (they are called guts in the slate cliffs around Boscastle). The sea exploits a narrow weakness to form a deep, steep-sided cleft, often only accessible to experienced climbers. The Great Zawn at Rosemergy near Gurnard's Head is one of the largest, with sheer sides determined by the jointing system.

As the coast retreated inland, more resistant sections of a cliff were left as foreshore stacks or islets, accessible at low tide. The coast at Bedruthan Steps is the best known example of this. With further retreat, some stacks remain far offshore, such as the twin Bawden Rocks off St Agnes Head, or rocks off Land's End and the Lizard Point. The powerful action of the sea may wear a stack down until it becomes a reef, only exposed at low water. The most notorious of these for shipping are the granite Seven Stones Reef, between Land's End and Scilly, and the Manacles off the coast near St Keverne.

Wave-cut platforms, or abrasion platforms, are formed where the sea cuts and planes a bench as it advances inland. The wider platforms suggest that sea level stood still for a considerable period, although it is argued that as the wave energy would be dissipated and erosive action slowed, it would need a steadily rising sea level to form such a wide bench. In the relatively short post-glacial period when it settled at its present level, the sea could not have had time to create some of the platforms, and indeed the cliffs, seen today. It would appear that the sea is merely excavating pre-existing platforms and cliffs. The wave-cut platform and notch at Porthleven, for example, are believed to be earlier than the Hoxnian interglacial. Wave-cut platforms are generally covered at the highest tides, but there are examples of fossil platforms a few feet higher than present sea level. Godrevy has a good one, associated with the fine exposure of raised beach in the cliff behind. The platform gives added protection to the cliff by retarding erosion.

CHANGING SEA LEVELS

During the Pleistocene, sea level varied considerably above and below its present level. It fell by as much as 300 ft [90 m] below the present during the main glaciations because of the huge volume of water locked up in the ice. When the ice melted in the interglacials, sea level rose again. Raised beaches are evidence for levels higher than today, and the overlying 'head' from the last glaciation (Devensian) shows they must date from at least the preceding Ipswichian interglacial. Raised beaches usually lie on a wave-cut platform and have a base of rounded pebbles (often cemented together) with further sand and beach material. The raised beach at Godrevy is at about 15 ft [4.5 m] above the present one, while there is one at 65 ft [20 m] at Penlee Quarry, Newlyn, where coarse beach deposits are banked against an ancient cliff. They are common around the coast, but are difficult to correlate as they stand at slightly different levels.

In Cornwall, sea level has been rising relative to the land during the Flandrian or post-glacial period of the last 10,000 years, so we see a coast of submergence. Submerged or fossil forests witness where trees once flourished on low ground close to a former shoreline. These may be revealed at very low tide, perhaps after storms have shifted the sand, and around

thirty sites include Daymer Bay, Maenporth, Millendreath, Mount's Bay, Pendower Beach, Porth, Porthmissen and Portreath. Evidence is also seen in the Isles of Scilly, where old field walls are revealed on some sand flats at low tide. It is not hard to see that a fall in sea level of just 30 ft [9 m] would restore Scilly to one or possibly two large islands, as was certainly the case in about 8,000 BC. The legend of the lost land of Lyonesse between Land's End and Scilly is perhaps a distant folk memory of this gradual drowning of the landscape during post-glacial times.

Rias are major features of a drowned coastline, and Cornwall is a classic location. During the Ice Age the sea fell long enough for rejuvenated rivers to cut deep valleys, aided by meltwater floods, until the post-glacial rise in sea level drowned their lower courses. These rias are seen in plan as finger-like inlets in the coast. The Fal estuary is the finest example, with the former valley course meandering as the deep-water channel through the Carrick Roads to the open sea. The Fal's branching tributaries include Restronguet, Truro, Tresillian and Porthcuel. Although there is still deep

THE FAL ESTUARY – A CLASSIC RIA

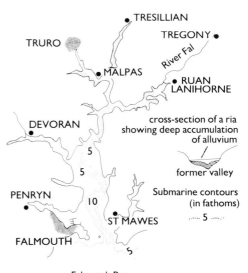

Falmouth Bay

Loe Pool from the air.

water, much alluvium has infilled the old channels, greatly increased by waste from mine-workings being brought down by rivers in historical times. The Truro River escaped much of this by constant dredging and has remained navigable to shipping right up to the city centre. In contrast, the higher end of Restronguet Pool was said to have had 42 ft [13 m] of water at low spring tides in 1698, but this was dry by 1855. The Fal itself was once navigable to Tregony Bridge, but now the tide only rises to Ruan Lanihorne, 2³/₄miles [4.4km] downstream.

Likewise, the Fowey is now barely navigable to Lostwithiel, while at Par, the estuary was tidal and vessels up to 80 tons could navigate to Ponts Mill in the early eighteenth century. At nearby Pentewan, forest remains were found beneath more than 50 ft [15 m] of marine and estuarine deposits, further evidence for a rise in sea level and the complete silting of a former estuary. Indeed, the tiny port of Pentewan has suffered the same fate. Other rivers with rias are the Tamar, Lynher, Looe, Helford and Cober (blocked by Loe Bar) on the south coast, and the Hayle, Gannel and Camel on the north. Polperro and Boscastle are similar examples of small rias with very steep-sided valleys.

FEATURES OF DEPOSITION

Not all coastal geology is related to erosion. Beach material is deposited and could be the conglomerate rock of the future. The fore-shore is that part of the beach between high and low water marks. Storm beaches are banks of material thrown up at the back of the beach during a combination of the highest tides

and rough weather, and waves may not reach here until the next period of severe gales. Thus, they form protection to any cliffs behind. The beach material usually consists of boulders, pebbles and sand of broken-down rock eroded from the cliffs in the vicinity, with additional shell fragments. The north coast, however, has a high proportion of shell sand which has resulted in blown sand dunes. Pebbles of flint and slag may have been introduced to beaches near some ports, having been brought in trading vessels as ballast. The beach at Charlestown is one such example.

Cornwall has an unusual beach on the east side of Mount's Bay in the shape of Loe Bar. This is known as a bay-bar, a high shingle bank blocking the former Cober estuary or ria. It is about 200 yards [180 m] wide, and holds back the fresh-water Loe Pool. The bank contains 75% or more of flint and chert, derived from chalk out in the English Channel. Similar but smaller bars hold back the marshes at Marazion (which overly a submerged forest) and the Swanpool at Falmouth.

The silting of estuaries by mine waste has been noted above, but human factors have been involved on the coast too. For example, beaches around Porthoustock and Porthallow on the Lizard peninsula have grown seawards by the accretion of waste spilled into the sea from nearby clifftop quarries. This progradation of the beach at Porthoustock has extended it by about 100 yards [90m] in the last century.

Dunes were perhaps initiated in the past during a drier climate, when the light shelly sand was blown by the wind. They are mainly a feature of the north coast, especially at Upton and Gwithian Towans (Hayle), Penhale Sands (Perranporth), with others at Holywell Bay, Crantock, Constantine (where they cross the Trevose peninsula to Harlyn Bay), and Daymer Bay. Much of the Camel estuary is filled with this shelly sand, unlike the alluvium so characteristic elsewhere. On the south coast, smaller dunes can be seen at Marazion, Praa Sands and Gunwalloe Church Cove.

ECONOMIC GEOLOGY

Extractive industries have played an important part in Cornwall's economy.

MINERALS

Cornwall's diverse mineral resources have been a great source of wealth over the centuries of exploitation. Tin and copper are the best known mining industries, but other metals which were mined include lead, zinc, manganese, iron, silver, antimony, wolfram, uranium, etc. The ruins of engine houses still stand amid the scars of exploitation in the principal mining districts around St Just, St Ives, Camborne–Redruth, Wendron, St Day–Gwennap, St Agnes–Perranporth, St Austell, Liskeard and Callington–Gunnislake. Other mines were sunk in places far from these main districts. Today, only one mine is at work: South Crofty at Camborne. Low tin prices forced Wheal Jane at Bissoe and Geevor at Pendeen to close by 1991.

Geevor at Pendeen, to suspend operations. Much has been written about mining (including a book in this series). Places to visit include the preserved Cornish beam engines at East Pool Mine (near South Crofty) and Levant, and the Geevor Mining Museum. Other museums with relics of past mining include the Royal Cornwall Museum at Truro and Wayside Museum at Zennor.

Shaft headgear at Pendarves tin mine, 1968.

ROCKS

Quarrying has been another important extractive industry in Cornwall. Granite moorstones have been cut and taken ever since prehistoric times. Quarries developed in the nineteenth century, when huge blocks of granite were dressed for civil engineering works such as docks, breakwaters, lighthouses and London's bridges, in addition to kerbstones, monuments, tombstones and architectural purposes. The busiest district was Carnmenellis behind the main granite shipping port of Penryn. Other quarrying took place around Lamorna and north of Penzance, at Hingston Down, Kit Hill, Luxulyan, and on south-east and north-west Bodmin Moor. Today, only five quarries produce 'dimension' stone mostly for cladding or memorials. The most famous is De Lank Quarry at St Breward on Bodmin Moor, which furnished granite for the Eddystone and Bishop Rock lighthouses in the last century. Granite is also worked for roadstone in three Carnmenellis quarries, as well as at Hingston Down, Tregarden (Hensbarrow) and Castle-an-Dinas (Land's End).

Elvan was often quarried for roadstone, but some types made a good building stone, such as at Newham near Truro, and Pentewan. Twentieth-century roadstone quarries in igneous rocks are scattered throughout the county, but notably at Penlee (Newlyn), Porthoustock, Dean Point, Menheniot, Greystone Bridge (Tamar) and beside the Lynher estuary.

Slate for building, especially roofing, developed an export trade in the Middle Ages, and so-called 'helling stones' were shipped coastwise as far as the Netherlands. The most famous quarry is Delabole, still at work after perhaps seven centuries and over 500 ft [152 m] deep. Other quarries are active between here and Trebarwith, but past slate workings in this part of north Cornwall can be seen along the cliffs on both sides of Tintagel. Before the railway came in 1899, slate was shipped from Port Gaverne and Tintagel. A dark slate was exploited at St Neot, where several workings were underground, akin to the Welsh slate mines. One, at Carnglaze, is open to the public. Hundreds of small quarries in slates of lesser quality once supplied local buildings needs.

Serpentinite from the Lizard is an attractive ornamental stone which can be easily carved, turned and polished. It was worked for decorative panels, fireplaces, tombstones, urns and other ornamental pieces in the last century, and souvenirs are still produced in small workshops on the Lizard.

Buildings are the end result of exploiting the county's rocks and are perhaps the best place to observe the variety of types and uses to which they have been put. Churches are always good for stones which are no longer quarried, such as Polyphant, Cataclews or Tartan Down. Other historic buildings contain imported stones of interest. Truro Cathedral, for example, displays a variety of stones, and a useful little guide can be obtained there. Surprisingly, King Arthur's Hall at Tintagel has a notable selection of Cornish stones in its fabric. There are of course the commoner granites,

slates and sandstones which have been put to good use.

The china clay industry is now a major employer in Cornwall, with the most important workings to the north of St Austell. The great waste tips are mostly of quartz and feldspar. China stone is still worked in this district for the ceramic industry. The harder variety can be carved more easily than true granite and was quarried in times past for local building stone. The museum of the industry is at Wheal Martyn near St Austell.

Younger sands and clays, such as around St Agnes Beacon, have been worked commercially. Sea sand has been taken at Gwithian, Padstow and Bude, the shelly varieties mainly as a source of lime for spreading on the acid Cornish soils.

A futuristic application of Cornwall's geology was undertaken in the hot rocks project at Rosemanowas Quarry near Penryn, where deep bore holes exploited the structure and heated within the granite to produce hot water for potential power generation.

Tor Down granite quarry, near St Breward.   *P.S.*

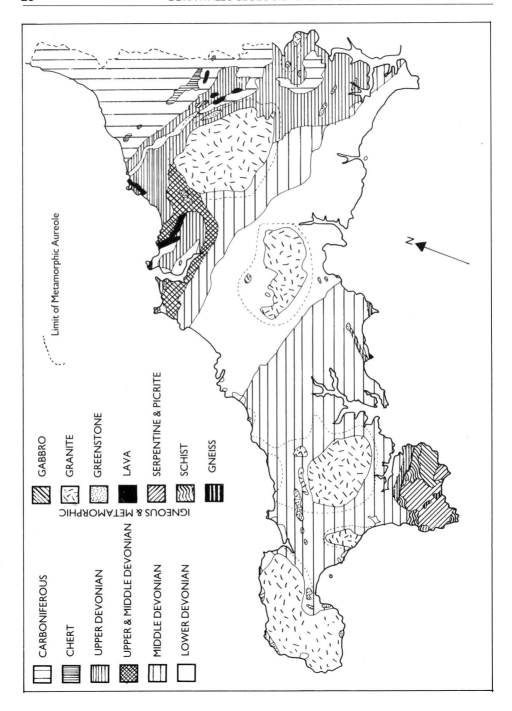

Limit of Metamorphic Aureole

IGNEOUS & METAMORPHIC

GABBRO

GRANITE

GREENSTONE

LAVA

SERPENTINE & PICRITE

SCHIST

GNEISS

CARBONIFEROUS

CHERT

UPPER DEVONIAN

UPPER & MIDDLE DEVONIAN

MIDDLE DEVONIAN

LOWER DEVONIAN

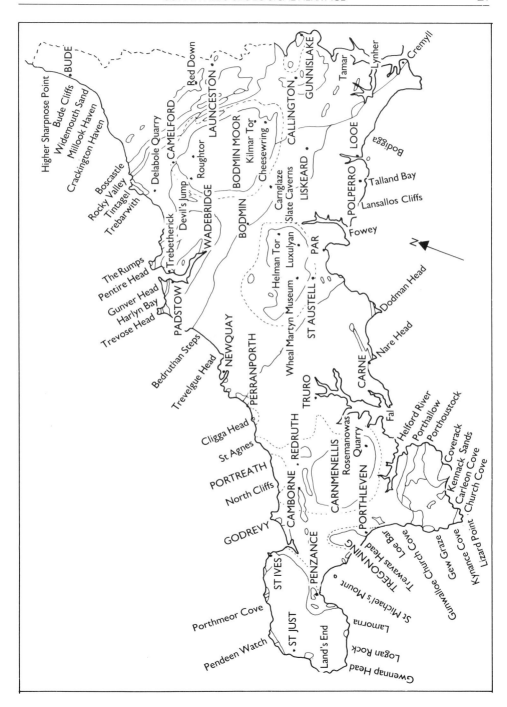

IN THE FIELD

This gazetteer lists a selection of places of geological interest around the county. Some are sites of specific interest, while others encompass several points in the general vicinity. Inevitably, most are along the fine coastline, where the best exposures of rocks and structures can be seen. Quarries and road and rail cuttings are also worth investigating, especially when freshly excavated. The waste tips of the mines contain mineral specimens, although these have become less abundant in recent years.

For convenience, the county has been divided into sections covering museum collections, the coasts and inland Cornwall. This is not based on geological boundaries. The sites in the north and south coast sections each progress eastwards from a starting point at Land's End, while the inland section is arranged alphabetically. Grid references are given and the Ordnance Survey 1:50,000 maps should be adequate to locate the sites. For greater interest, the British Geological Survey maps show the surface geology and cover the county at the same scale.

A code for amateur geologists: Make sure there is public access. When on the coast, watch out for dangerous cliffs and falling rocks, and do not underestimate rough seas and incoming tides! Reference to a reliable tide table is advised before visiting some coastal sites. Mine workings are dangerous and should only be entered by well-equipped experts. Do not damage features if collecting specimens, as this ruins them for everyone else.

MUSEUM COLLECTIONS

The three important geological collections in Cornwall, are at Truro, Pool and Penzance. The last of these is the Museum of the Royal Geological Society of Cornwall, in the west wing of St John's Hall, Alverton Street, Penzance, which is undergoing refurbishment and is not yet fully open to the public. However, in the same district the Penzance and District Museum, Geevor Tin Mining Museum and Zennor Wayside Museum have some minerals on display. The St Ives Museum has a section on mining. Most local museums usually have something of geological interest, such as minerals at Bodmin and Camborne, or displays on local slate and granite quarrying at Camelford's North Cornwall Museum.

ROYAL CORNWALL MUSEUM

River Street, Truro, TRI 2SJ.
Telephone: (0872) 72205.
A visit to the museum's world-famous collection of minerals is essential to appreciate the variety and beauty of these specimens, of which some are extremely rare. They are a source of inspiration for the would-be collector, although very rarely can such good examples be found in the field. Nevertheless, making one's own collection, however humble, can be rewarding and a great aid to understanding Cornwall's geology. Inevitably, most of the finest specimens have come from Cornish mines, but not just the famous and important ones, as very obscure mines have also yielded rare minerals. The minerals are displayed in the Rashleigh Gallery, for its core includes part of the late eighteenth-century collection of Philip Rashleigh, said to be one of the finest in Europe and 'uniquely rich in copper minerals.' Specimens from other collectors are also represented.

Types of copper ores include native copper, in a dendritic form from mines in the Gwennap district and elsewhere; a variety of cuprite showing red crystals of chalcotrichite or hair copper, also from Gwennap; tile ore, or 'ziegelerz', an earthy brick-red ore from Phoenix Mine; chalcophyllite (arsenate of copper) from Gwennap; liroconite (arsenate of copper) from Wheal Gorland, possibly the largest crystal in the world; olivenite (arsenate of copper) from Gwennap; chalcocite (enriched sulphide of copper), locally called 'Redruthite'; and azurite (blue carbonate of copper), which includes a very fine specimen from South Caradon Mine, from the Williams of Scorrier collection.

Of the tin ores, varieties of cassiterite include black diamond tin from Carn Brea Mine; St Agnes tin, said to be best in world; a world famous specimen from Wheal Coates, showing the partial replacement of feldspar by cassiterite; and pebbles of wood tin found in streams at several localities. Stannite is a rare sulphide of tin (25%), copper (36%) and iron (2%). It was identified from Wheal Rock, St Agnes, in 1785 by Rudolphe Erich Raspe, who called it 'bell-metal ore' because of its colour. Raspe was the assay master at Dolcoath Mine at this time, when he also wrote *The Adventures of Baron Munchausen*, for which he is better known. An altered specimen, or isostannite, was obtained from Cligga Mine as recently as 1975.

Varieties of lead ores are galena, with examples of cubes from West Chiverton Mine, mimetite (arsenate of lead) from Wheal Alfred, pyromorphite (phosphate of lead), and white needles or 'straws' of cerussite (carbonate of lead) from Pentire Glaze. These are among the world's finest specimens. There are notable large crystals of wolframite from East Pool and Cligga Mines. Among the other minerals are antimony, native arsenic said to have come from Dolcoath Mine in about 1840, bismuth, bournonite (sulphide of antimony), wheel ore (endellionite) from Herodsfoot Mine, cobalt (rare in Cornwall), very rare horse tooth iron (siderite) from Wheal Maudlin, Lanlivery, good specimens of molybdenite, still found during quarrying operations at Hingston Down Quarry, niccolite, a very rare Cornish mineral from Gerrans Bay, and stibnite. Uranium ores include black uranite (pitchblende) from Wheal Trenwith, emerald green torbenite, and lemon yellow autinite found coating a joint plane at Cheesewring Quarry.

There are specimens too of Cornish gold and silver. There is a gold nugget which was found in the Carnon valley tin stream works in 1808, and a necklace made in 1802 from Ladock gold is displayed in the main hall. Silver specimens include wires of native silver from, for example, Herland Mine, Gwinear.

Some rock specimens are displayed, including gabbro from Dean Quarry which shows the secondary silicate minerals analcite, chabazite, natrolite (needles) and stilbite coating the joints. From the same Lizard district, there are soapstones and serpentines.

Cornwall's rather poorly preserved fossils are also displayed, including ammonites, brachiopods (the 'Delabole butterfly'), corals, fish, gastropods and trilobites.

CAMBORNE SCHOOL OF MINES GEOLOGICAL MUSEUM

Pool, Redruth, TR15 3SE.
Telephone: (0209) 714866.

The museum opened in 1975 and has as its centre the mineral collection of Robert Hunt (1807–87), who was a founder of miners' education and Keeper of the Mining Record Office. There are also the Davey and Thomas collections. These are worldwide minerals from Africa, Australia, North and South America and Europe, many from the mining districts to which Cornish miners went to work.

Of local Cornish interest, there are small displays on extractive industries including minerals, stone and china clay. There are two notable large exhibits. The first is a thin slab of native copper found in veins of steatite at Wheal Unity (Ghostcroft Mine), Mullion. This mine produced the largest mass of native copper ever found in Britain – a block measuring 30 ft x 4 ft 6 ins [9.1 m x 1.4 m], and shown at the Great Exhibition of 1851. Another mineral mass, donated recently, is a huge piece from Mount Wellington Mine containing delicate silica shells filled with a bright blue liquid rich in copper, iron and zinc sulphates – formed by the oxidation of chalcopyrite and sphalerite by downward moving oxidising solutions at a late stage in the evolution of the lode.

The Camborne School of Mines site is within a half mile [0.8 km] of the working South Crofty Mine and the National Trust's preserved winding and pumping beam engines at East Pool Mine.

That part of the peninsula which stretches north-eastwards from Land's End to the Devon border at Marsland Mouth has a rugged grandeur which is broken only by the Camel estuary, and to a lesser extent at Hayle, the Gannel and Boscastle.

LAND'S END TO PENDEEN WATCH
[SW 3412253 to SW 380360]

A varied coastline, mostly granite but also killas, hornfels and greenstone within the metamorphic aureole from Cape Cornwall to Pendeen Watch. The greenstone can be seen at Kenidjack Cliff (where it has been quarried) and Botallack Head and many of the cliffs are indented with zawns. Surface geology includes blown sand at Sennen Cove (Whitesand Bay) and a raised beach at Porth Nanven. This is in the area of the St Just mining district, and the clifftops from Cape Cornwall onwards are covered with the relics of tin and copper mining. The most famous mines down on the cliffs are Botallack and Levant. The Geevor Tin Mining Museum [telephone: (0736) 788662] is at Pendeen. Just east of Pendeen Watch the

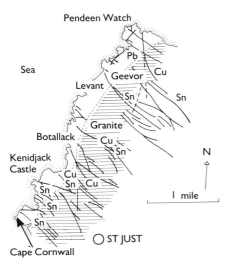

Mineral lodes between Cape Cornwall and Pendeen Watch, extend from granite into the metamorphic aureole beneath the sea.

junction with the granite occurs in Portheras Cove.

PORTHMEOR COVE
[SW 426375]

Only reached by walking along the coastal footpath or descending from the B3306 coast road near Higher Porthmeor just west of the Gurnard's Head Hotel. The cove is best visited at low tide. The east side shows the roof zone of the granite, with veins and dykes of aplite and pegmatite extending into the country rocks. Note the great depth of 'head' cut into by the stream which flows down the valley into the cove. Further east, beyond the greenstone Gurnard's and Zennor Heads, a complex granite/killas junction can be seen at Wicca Pool [SW 465400].

ST IVES
[SW 520412]

Greenstone exposures in the metamorphic aureole are easily accessible at St Ives. Where washed by the sea, it is a blackish stone, fine or medium grained and rather greasy when wet. It is exposed at The Island or St Ives Head, but is best seen across Porthmeor Beach at Carrick Dhu or Man's Head [SW 512410]. Note the low cliff of 'head' between here and Clodgy Point.

GODREVY
[SW 580430]

On the east side of St Ives Bay. The raised beach is well seen where the steps descend from the National Trust car park. The cliff section reveals the former wave-cut platform (on dipping and contorted slates) on top of which is pebbly material up to 8 ft [2.4 m] thick and cemented at the base with iron or manganese oxide. This raised beach is overlain by 'head' and blown sand. Just north of the steps, the sea is cutting a new platform into the old one (already honeycombed by weathering). There is a cliff and residual section of cemented shelly sand on top of the old platform. Good folding is displayed in the cliff section of

Raised beach, Godrevy. *P.S.*

slates just north towards Godrevy Point. Beyond is Godrevy Island and lighthouse, an example of an offshore islet. The coast around to Navax Point [SW 592436] is deeply indented with coves and caves. South-west from Godrevy can be seen the great expanse of Gwithian and Upton Towans, great dunes of blown sand behind 3 miles [4.8 km] of beach. The Red River, formerly heavily laden with mine waste from the Camborne area, enters the sea at Godrevy.

NORTH CLIFFS
[SW 603400 to SW 650454]

The long line of slate and sandstone cliffs from the notorious Hell's Mouth to Portreath are in the Falmouth and Portscatho Series of pro-bable Middle Devonian age. They are topped by a fine marine erosion platform, here at just over 250 ft [76 m], but belonging to the widespread 430 ft [130 m] platform. Towards Portreath, offshore islands include Gull Rock and` Samphire and Crane Islands. Ralph's

Cupboard is a deep zawn just west of Portreath [SW 645451]. Occasionally, storms reveal a submerged forest on the beach at Portreath.

ST AGNES
[SW 710505]

St. Agnes Beacon stands up from the coastal platform, as it was once an island in the Pliocene sea. There are deposits of clays and sands around its foot on the north side. The former was once dug as a refractory clay and candle clay (the Cornish miners used it to attach tallow candles to their helmets). This is a good area for minerals, and mining activity is very apparent between Chapel Porth [SW 697495] and Trevellas Porth [SW 725519] – the St Agnes mining district. The engine houses of the Wheal Coates tin mine [SW 700502] are prominent on the coast at Chapel Porth, from which a walk along the beach at low tide shows a good exposure of the main Towan-wrath Lode in the cliff.

CLIGGA HEAD
[SW 738537]

A small outcrop of rather weak granite on the coast. Well-developed greisen veins can be seen in the quarry near the top of the Head. There are also greisen veins with cassiterite and wolfram, best seen at the foot of the cove below. The cliffs have been extensively mined hereabouts and the reddish cliffs to the west are honeycombed with workings. They can be examined by making a careful descent to the foot of the main cove and traversing the beach at low tide. Further south, green copper-

Greisen veins in the quarry at Cligga Head. *P.S.*

Prison Cove, at Hanover Cove (Cligga Head), is the result of differential erosion by the sea. The cliffs are 250 feet high.

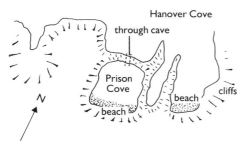

Not to scale

staining streaks the cliffs of Hanover Cove [SW 738531]. The nearby Prison Cove is a major feature where the sea has broken into a huge vertical-sided opening.

PERRANPORTH
[SW 755545]

The resort, once a mining centre, is dominated on the east side by Penhale Sands, extensive dunes of blown sand which overwhelmed past settlements, including St Piran's oratory. There are more dunes at Holywell Bay [SW 765595]. The Great Perran Iron Lode is exposed at the north end of Penhale Beach [SW764573]. On the west side of Perranporth, the cliffs of Droskyn Point have caves and arches, enlarged by mining.

TREVELGUE HEAD
[SW 825630]

The outer part of the headland is separated by a narrow cleft (crossed by a foot bridge),

making this an island at high tide. Alongside, Porth is a sandy inlet or ria, far smaller than The Gannel [SW 800610] which lies south of Newquay. The cliffs on the north side of Trevelgue Head are indented with large caves, including the now destroyed Banqueting Hall which was used for public entertainments until the 1930s. The great beach (at low tide) of Watergate Bay sweeps north-eastwards.

BEDRUTHAN STEPS
[SW 848694]

A line of stacks along the beach makes this a popular section of cliff scenery north of Newquay. The view from the clifftop is a familiar subject for photography, but the place is best appreciated by making the steep descent and walking the beach at low tide. Beware of incoming tide, it is very easy to get cut off! The rock is mostly fairly soft Middle Devonian slate. The stacks have names, such as Diggory's Island, Queen Bess Rock, Samaritan Rock, Redcove Island, Pendarves Island and Carnewas Island. A cave through the cliff gives access to the south shore. There is a National Trust car park and information centre in a converted building of the nineteenth-century Carnewas iron mine. Park Head is the prominent headland to the north, a small exposure of quartz-diabase [SX 841708].

TREVOSE HEAD
[SW 851763]

A fine coastal viewpoint. Jagged stacks, the Bull and Quies, stand out in a line seawards from Dinas Head just south of the lighthouse. A greenstone intrusion here (exposed in a

Broken wave cut platform, Porthcothan, between Bedruthan Steps and Trevose.   *P.S.*

Bedruthan Steps.

quarry) has greatly altered the surrounding rocks which include thin bands of limestone. South again, the Round Hole is similar to that at Trevone, where the roof of a large sea cave has collapsed on the cliff top.

HARLYN BAY
[SW 876755]

There are blown sand dunes between here and Constantine Bay [SW 858750], across the low neck of the Trevose Head peninsula. The beach at Harlyn Bay itself has an exposure of rock-hard cemented shell sand near the high water mark. Cataclews Point [SW 872761] is on the west side, where a variety of rocks includes limestones and Cataclews Stone, a blue-grey proterobase sill, which can be carved. It was quarried here in medieval times for church furnishings, and is seen at its best in the piers and font of nearby St Merryn church.

MARBLE CLIFFS
[SW 891763]

About 140 thin bands of alternate limestone and shale make this an interesting exposure just a short walk from Trevone, past the Round Hole and near Porthmissen Bridge. Gunver Head is just beyond.

GUNVER HEAD
[SW 895771]

Lower, Middle and Higher Merope Islands are three high stacks of Upper Devonian slate separated from the main cliff by the narrow Tregudda Gorge. The north stack is a thin pinnacle. This is an unusual section of coastline, with the Marble Cliff to the west and greenstone exposed further north-east at Stepper Point [SW 915783], where there is a disused roadstone quarry at the mouth of the Camel.

TREBETHERICK POINT
[SW 926780]

Trebetherick lies on the east side of the Camel estuary, between Daymer Bay and Polzeath which are normally associated with family holidays rather than geology. Green and purple slates are exposed on the shoreline, while the

cliff exposes two layers of 'head' and raised beaches at about 10 ft [3 m] and 55 ft [17 m] containing greenstone erratics perhaps derived from ice floes. The sand dunes of St Enodoc lie to the south of Daymer Bay and Brae Hill.

PENTIRE HEAD AND THE RUMPS
[SW 930807]

Spectacular cliff scenery north of Polzeath, with the main geological interest in the pillow lava here. Sections of these pillowy forms can be seen in the cliffs and also in small outcrops beside the coastal footpath. Rumps Point is the site of Cornwall's finest iron-age cliff castle, the narrow neck being of softer slates and the double headland of more resistant greenstone. There is a car park for this National Trust property at Pentire Farm, close to the site of the Pentireglaze Mine which produced lead, silver and antimony. Eastwards, pillow lava is

Marble Cliffs.

exposed in the cliffs of Trevan Point [SW 961801] on the east side of Lundy Bay, and Doyden Point [SW 967807] and Kellan Head [SW 970812] near Port Quin.

TREBARWITH STRAND
[SX 048864]

Trebarwith Strand has a superb beach which, it is worth remembering, disappears at high tide. Altered volcanic rocks in the Trebarwith valley are exposed near the shore, where they have been pot-holed by the rejuvenated stream. To the north, a low-angle fault has reversed the normal geological sequence by thrusting Upper Devonian slates over Lower Carboniferous slates. Above Hole Beach, Lanterdan Quarry [SX 051872] has been worked in a Devonian

Lanterdan quarry pillar, near Trebarwith.   *P.S.*

slate in which some fossils can be found. The quarry has pinnacles of unworked rock, the tallest being about 70 ft [21 m] high.

TINTAGEL
[SX 050890]

Around Tintagel, the Devonian and Carboniferous slates are mixed with volcanic rocks and further complicated by low-angle faults or thrusts. For example, the south cliff of Tintagel Island (best viewed from near the church) shows Tintagel volcanics and dark Barras Nose slates (Lower Carboniferous) to have been sandwiched by faults between Upper Devonian slates. The west face below the castle's Outer Ward shows evidence of low-angle and later steep faulting. It is possible to descend to Tintagel Haven, where the sea has exploited weaknesses in the fault zone and eroded through-caves beneath the castle and across the beach towards Barras Nose. A small lead lode can be inspected from the beach just seawards of the so-called Merlin's Cave beneath the castle. This was worked in the last century. The sea is cutting the cove back so rapidly that the valley stream cascades to the

beach by a waterfall. There are disused slate quarries along the cliffs to the south, where the Tintagel Youth Hostel is in a building of the former Lamb's House Quarry among the waste on the cliff top. An unlikely venue for seeing Cornish stones in use as a building material is King Arthur's Hall in Tintagel village.

ROCKY VALLEY
[SX 072895]

A true mini-gorge in Devonian slates, with potholes, waterfalls and all the features of a fast-flowing stream before it suddenly meets the sea. Also known as Trevillet Gorge, this picturesque valley can be reached from the coastal footpath or a path from the B3263. Up the valley, a waterfall plunges into a basin known as St Nectan's Kieve [SX 081885]. All this is the result of downcutting by a rejuvenated stream after a rapid fall in base level.

BOSCASTLE
[SX 095915]

The deep Valency valley meets the coast as a tiny ria, with a last meander giving protection to the tidal harbour. On the north side, at Penally Point, there are good exposures of intensely folded rocks, but on a small scale. These slates and siltstones belong to the Boscastle Measures (Lower Carboniferous). There is a good walk along the cliffs south-west to Tintagel, although access to the rock exposures is difficult except at Rocky Valley and Bossiney. A shorter walk in the other direction leads to Pentargon Cove [SX 107919], where there is a fine waterfall. Ruck folds at the foot of the cliff give the appearance of petrified tree trunks. A little north is Fire Beacon Point, the seaward limit of the Lower Carboniferous cherts.

CRACKINGTON HAVEN
[SX 142969]

Two deep valleys meet here, where 'head' is exposed at the back of the cove. There are impressive cliffs of folded shales and sandstones hereabouts. Just north, around Pencannow Point, the next valley is cut by the eroding sea, so that the stream now cascades over a

Folded rocks in Millook cliffs.

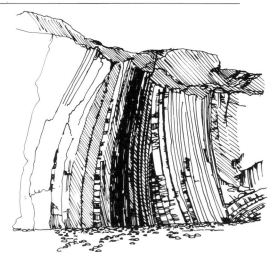

Inclined strata, Bude.

waterfall [SX 142975]. Two miles [3.2 km] SSW, is High Cliff the highest in Cornwall at 731 ft [223 m], although it is not sheer. It provides a good north view over The Strangles beach, with the curious arched Northern Door and Cambeak Point beyond. Rusey Beach [SX 125940] is the centre of a fault zone.

MILLOOK HAVEN
[SX 185002]

Highly impressive zig-zag folds in sandstones and shales of the Crackington Measures (Carboniferous) are guaranteed to justify the difficult drive down steep narrow lanes. A pebbly storm beach gives some protection to the foot of this cliff on the north side of the Haven.

WIDEMOUTH SAND
[SS 199026]

A raised beach overlies a clayey 'head' material, and is itself covered by blown sand. Folded rocks (Bude Formation) in the cliffs are well worth following north past Lower and Higher Longbeak to Bude. This is a serious expedition except at low tide. There are some escape routes, or a shorter route can be followed from Upton (see Bude Cliffs). To the south, folds and faults are exposed in the wave-cut platform upon which stands Black Rock, a stack of more resistant slump breccia.

BUDE CLIFFS
[SS 200047 to SS 202086]

The coastline on both sides of Bude Haven has long exposures of highly contorted sandstone and shale bands, inclined from the horizontal to vertical and all angles between. A superb traverse along the shore from Upton [SS 200047], one mile [1.6 km] south of Bude, is best started two hours before low tide. It requires some scrambling and every headland or rib turned reveals a new delight. The rock can be loose, so take great care when at the foot of these cliffs. There is an escape up the cove just before Compass Point [SS 199063] which can be rounded only at low tide. Note the Whale Rock, a pericline exposed on the beach between the point and the breakwater at Bude Haven [SS 200064]. Folded cliffs can be seen more easily by walking at low tide along the sandy beach north from Bude past Maer Cliff to Northcott Mouth [SS 202086], or beyond.

Rock strata on Bude beach. *P.S.*

HIGHER AND LOWER SHARPNOSE POINTS
[SS 195147 & SS 195127]

Higher Sharpnose Point is reached along the coastal footpath from Morwenstow. Steeply dipping strata lies at right angles to the coast, giving impressive slabs on the south side of the point. On the north side, the Tidna stream follows the strike of the strata in a hanging valley before cascading over a waterfall. 1 1/4 miles [2 km] south, Lower Sharpnose Point [SS 195127] has three steep and narrow fins of sandstone projecting seawards. The top of the point is dominated by the dish aerials of a communications station. Gull Rock [SS204172] is one mile north of Morwenstow church off Marsland Cliff, at the border with Devon.

Intensely folded strata at Gull Rock.

SOUTH COAST

The coast from Land's End, around the Lizard peninsula and as far as the Tamar River and Devon border. It is a coastline indented with rias, including the Helford, Fal, Fowey, Looe, Lynher and Tamar estuaries. High cliffs are a feature only of the Atlantic coasts of the Lizard and Land's End peninsulas.

LAND'S END TO GWENNAP HEAD
[SW 341253 to SW 366215]

The regular jointing in the granite has produced the famous castellated cliffs at Land's End, which have stood for centuries against the full force of the Atlantic. Just south are the Armed Knight and Enys Dodnan stacks, and then the finest granite cliffs in Cornwall continue south-eastwards for 2 miles [3.2 km] to Porthgwarra. There are spectacular rocks and pinnacles at Pordenack Point, Carn Boel and Carn Barra. The weaker, more jointed granite has been eroded between the headlands, forming Nanjizal Bay and Pendower Cove. At Chair Ladder and Gwennap Head [SW 366215] there are sheer cliffs of stacked and pinnacled granite, again showing the jointing to good ef-

fect. A mile [1.6 km] offshore is the Runnel Stone, a dangerous reef marked by a bell buoy. Gwennap Head can be approached from Porthgwarra village and cove.

LOGAN ROCK
[SW 397220]

This is the most famous of all the Cornish logan stones, resting atop the dramatic promontory of Treryn Dinas which also has traces of an iron age cliff castle. The Logan Rock

The Logan Rock.   *P.S.*

Giant's Rock, Porthleven, with Trewavas Head beyond. *P.S.*

weighs an estimated 65 tons, which did not prevent it being dislodged in 1824 by Lieutenant Hugh Colvill Goldsmith, who was soon ordered to replace it! He did this to much acclaim, but the rock can no longer be moved with such ease as before.

LAMORNA COVE
[SW 451241]

The east side of the Lamorna valley has nineteenth-century granite quarries, with large waste tips. Rocks here and in the cove show well-developed feldspar crystals. The granite was shipped from the cove for works at Devonport Dockyard and the Longships and Wolf Rock lighthouses, but hazardous seas and the loss of popularity of this type of granite combined to close the quarries early this century. Just west at Tater-du [SW 440230] is a small exposure of greenstone on an otherwise all-granite coast.

TREWAVAS HEAD
[SW 597265]

The Tregonning granite outcrops along the coast between Praa Sands and Trequean, with impressive cliffs at Trewavas Head. Of the buttresses and pinnacles here, the Camel or Bishop Rock is the most prominent, so-named from its shape. There are two cliff-side engine houses of the Trewavas copper mine, and signs of minerals around the mine site at the top of the cliff. At Rinsey Cove [SW 593269], from which the head can be approached, note the junction of the granite and killas (hornfels). Towards Porthleven, there are sills of granite pegmatite exposed in the face of Tremearne Cliff [SW 609267].

PORTHLEVEN
[SW 624257]

Just west of the harbour is an extensive wave-cut platform of dark slate (the Pargodonnel Rocks), scalloped and potholed with deep narrow gullies which are remarkably similar to the karst scenery of limestone uplands. There are caves and undercutting in the low cliffs at the back. It is believed that these and the platform belong to an interglacial period which the sea is now re-excavating. An added bonus and chief point of interest, is the Giant's Rock, lying on the platform and exposed at low tide. It is a polished glacial erratic of a gneiss unknown in Britain, and presumably dropped by a stranded iceberg during the Ice Age. It is much rounded and estimates of its weight vary from 20 to 50 tons. The easiest descent is from near a memorial to drowned sailors beside the coastal footpath.

LOE BAR
[SW 643241]

Cornwall's answer to Slapton Sands in south Devon. There was once a tidal ria navigable to

PORTHLEVEN AND LOE BAR

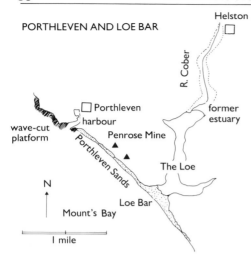

Helston, but now a great pebble bar blocks the Cober forming the freshwater Loe Pool. 75% of the rounded pebbles are flint or chert, derived from offshore chalk. Note the traces of lead mining (Wheal Penrose) along the cliffs between Loe Bar and Porthleven.

GUNWALLOE CHURCH COVE
[SW 661205]

There are small dunes of blown sand at the back of Gunwalloe Church Cove, where the historic church stands almost on the beach. The sea is eroding the weaker rock in the smaller cove just to the NW so that if left alone it will leave the church stranded on an island. From the beach at Jangye-ryn [SW 659207] can be seen a low cliff with dramatic folds in the slate and greywacke of the

Folded rocks at Jangye-ryn.   P.S.

Gramscatho Beds. Blown sand deposits lie on top.

GEW GRAZE
[SW 676144]

Best approached by a dramatic walk atop Kynance Cliff northwards from Kynance Cove towards Mullion. About half way, just past the deep zawn of Pigeon Ogo and before the great cliffs of Vellan Head, a large vein of soap stone was quarried at Gew Graze in the late eighteenth century for use in porcelain. Tiny veinlets can be seen in the side of the excavation.

KYNANCE COVE
[SW 685133]

The famous beauty spot, with cliffs and shore-line islands of tremolite-serpentinite. A fault on the east side of the cove separates this from bastite-serpentinite. The serpentinite cliffs are dull except where their colours are brought out by the polishing action of the sea. There are small dykes of granite in the cliffs on the west side. The main island is Asparagus Island, reached at low tide across the sand. Two stacks, the Steeple Rock and Sugar Loaf, stand between the island and mainland. On the island, the Devil's Letter Box and Bellows are blow-holes.

CHURCH COVE
[SW 715128]

There are hornblende-schists in Church Cove below Landewednack village, the same rocks which form the upstanding Bass Point to the

Talc veins in rocks at Landewednack.   P.S.

south [SW 715119]. The junction with bastite-serpentinite is exposed in a cliff-side quarry immediately to the north [SW 714129]. Veins of talc can be seen cutting the serpentinite here.

CARLEON COVE
[SW 728156]

The ruined serpentine factory near the beach operated from about 1855 until 1893. It was supplied in the last century with stone from Signal Staff Quarry, which was excavated along the cliffs between Kildown Point and Enys Head to the south [SW 726148].

KENNACK SANDS
[SW 734165]

Here are good exposures of the Kennack gneiss, often banded, as well as bastite-serpentinite, and small gabbro and basalt dykes.

COVERACK
[SW 784182]

The bastite-serpentinite on the shore is cut and re-cut by a sequence of dykes of troctolite, gabbro and epidiorite. Across the bay to the north-east, Lowland Point is an extensive flat area of raised beach [SW 803195].

Devoran, at the head of Restonguet Creek, was once a busy port but is now silted up.   P.S.

PORTHOUSTOCK AND PORTHALLOW
[SW 807218 & SW 797232]

There is an extensive area of roadstone quarries where gabbro and hornblende schists outcrop along the coast in the vicinity of St Keverne, between Dean Point and Porthallow. Of these, only Dean Quarry [SW 804204] is still worked and its products are shipped from a pier. Permission should therefore be sought if visiting. Crystals of zeolites (alumino-silicate minerals, as displayed in the Royal Cornwall Museum) are found here coating the joints in the gabbro. Basalt (epidiorite) dykes cut the gabbro at Manacle Point [SW 812214], and at Rosenython Quarry on the south side of the cove at Porthoustock [SW 807218]. The beach in this cove has advanced seawards since the quarries opened and started tipping waste into the sea at the beginning of the century. There are more old quarries in hornblende-schist from the north side of the cove, along the coast at Pencra Head and Porthkerris Point, to Porthallow [SW 797232]. Here, pinkish granite-gneiss, mica and hornblende-schist, serpentinite, phyllite and other rocks can be observed along the south shore. Northwards to Nare Point [SW 800251], the cliffs are in the Meneage Breccia, with broken blocks of Lizard rocks, slate, limestone of possible Silurian age, and large masses of Ordovician quartzite.

HELFORD RIVER
[SW 760265]

This east–west ria separates the Lizard peninsula from the rest of Cornwall. There are
finger-like branches to Gweek, Polwheveral
and Porth Navas, while Frenchman's Creek
and Gillan Harbour are on the south side.

FAL ESTUARY
[SW 830370]

One of the great natural harbours of the
world. A large ria, with many branches, to
Penryn, Mylor, Restronguet, Truro, Tresillian
and Percuil. A deepwater channel at King
Harry Passage allows the laying-up of large
ocean ships in times of trade depression, best
seen by boat (a rewarding summer service
operates between Truro and Falmouth).

CARNE BEACH
[SW 905383]

There is a raised beach here, cemented at the
base and resting on a fossil wave-cut platform.
The old beach and overlying 'head' are
exposed in the low cliffs on both sides of the
modern beach, at the east end of Pendower
Beach in Gerrans Bay. Low cliffs in this area
show that little erosion is taking place. Just to
the east are tor-like outcrops of Ordovician
quartzite, known as Tregeagle's Quoits, legend
having it that they were hurled here from the
north coast by Dozmary Pool's giant Tregeagle.

NARE HEAD
[SW 917370]

The gentle coast of Gerrans Bay contrasts with

Carne beach, site of a raised beach.   *P.S.*

the upstanding Nare Nead, where the rock is
pillow lava. Offshore, is the islet of Gull Rock.

DODMAN POINT
[SX 002394]

A prominent headland rising to 373 ft [114 m]
between the Fal and Fowey harbours. Here
are the Dodman phyllites, separated from the
rest of Cornwall by a brecciated zone (Veryan
Series) from Veryan Bay to Gorran Haven
which contains Ordovician and Silurian quartzites and limestones. These outcrop for
example at Great Perhaver Beach [SX 018424]
and Porthluney Cove [SW 976400].

PAR
[SX 080530]

It is difficult to believe that the sea once
reached Ponts Mill [SX 073561] now that the
estuary has been so completely blocked with
alluvium and mineral waste. This is said to
reach a depth of 72 ft [22 m] at Par. Old cliffs
can be seen at Polmear at the east end of Par
Sands and others inland, for example near Par
railway station. There is a raised beach and
'head' material outside the harbour at Spit
Point [SX 076525]. To the west, the beach at
Carlyon Bay [SX 061522] is largely mine waste,
deposited on the shore by the stream diverted
through the cliff in 1842 to prevent silting at Par
harbour. Pentewan [SX 020472], the location
of the famous stone quarry, is another estuary
completely silted for similar reasons. Between
here and Par, the greenstone (quartz-diabase)
Black Head [SX 040480] stands out into St
Austell Bay.

LANSALLOS CLIFFS
[SX 170510]

Steeply dipping strata of Dartmouth Slates lie
parallel to the coast on the east side of Lantivet
Bay, where a fossil wave-cut platform protects
the cliff from erosion by the sea. Above, the
coastal footpath passes along the remnant of an
ancient raised platform at about 50 ft [15 m]
with a degraded cliff behind, now covered with
vegetation. Across the bay to the west the
rock changes to an upstanding exposure of
tough Meadfoot Beds at Pencarrow Head [SX
151504].

TALLAND BAY

[SX 225515]

A wave-cut platform crosses vertical strata of green and purple slates in the centre of the cove. These are the Dartmouth Slates of the Lower Devonian, which also appear along the cliffs around Watergate Bay on the north coast. The low cliff at the back of Talland Bay has evidence of a raised beach and 'head' material. It is possible to drive to Talland, but a pleasant walk along the cliff path from Polperro (a ria) shows more of the coast.

BODIGGA CLIFFS

[SX 274541]

There are very weak Lower Devonian slates and shales here. The whole cliff is unstable and slipping, with the base eroding rapidly. The beach is noted for a small outcrop of pink quartz. The easiest access is along the shore at mid to low tide from Millendreath Beach, itself the site of a submerged forest.

CREMYLL

[SX 456532]

The shoreline exposes the western end of the Devonian limestone which lies across the Tamar estuary in Plymouth, along the coast and in old quarries along the Hoe frontage to Cattedown and beyond. It is a distinct pale grey limestone with pinkish veins. Some of the stone quarried at Plymouth was shipped coastwise for limeburning and use in some buildings in Cornwall.

TAMAR AND LYNHER ESTUARIES

A large ria. The Tamar is shared with Devon, and the tide rises through a meandering gorge to reach Gunnislake [SX 436711]. The St Germans or Lynher River is all Cornish, and is best seen from the water or the main-line railway, which crosses three viaducts between Trematon and St Germans. There are several disused quarries in greenstones on the banks of the Lynher River branch, such as at Treluggan [SX 379583]. The much-silted tidal head of the River Tiddy branch can be seen from the A38 at Tideford.

INLAND CORNWALL

Inland Cornwall is dominated by granite, mining and landscape features. With the exception of the older Lizard rocks, the main country rocks of west Cornwall are slates and sandstones of probable Middle Devonian age. The west contains the greatest mining district of the county, in the granites of Carnmenellis, Carn Brea and Carn Marth, and the metamorphic aureole between Camborne and Redruth and at St Day. Here were famous mines such as Dolcoath (copper and tin), United and Consolidated (copper), and many others. Ruins are much in evidence, but the waste tips have diminished, removed as part of land rehabilitation schemes or for roadmaking and even processing for the last remnants of tin. This has therefore made mineral collecting increasingly more difficult. Other mines were centred on St Agnes and between Wendron and Marazion, while the Land's End granite had mining districts around St Just and St Ives. The last active tin mines have been in this west Cornwall. China clay occurs in the Land's End granite and has been worked near St Ives and St Just. China clay and china stone were worked in the past at Tregonning Hill, and even a small clay pit was worked in the Carnmenellis granite near Penryn.

East of Truro, the country rocks are mainly Lower Devonian in the south, progressing to Upper Devonian and Carboniferous in the north-east. Scattered igneous rocks include greenstones and lavas. There are two main granite uplands. Hensbarrow contains the major china clay district behind St Austell. Bodmin Moor has a distinct moorland landscape of its own, and was also the scene of mining and china clay working. The district around Kit Hill and Hingston Down, two small exposures of granite between Callington and

Rock basins on Carn Brea.   *P.S.*

the Tamar, was also extensively mined for minerals. Further mineralised areas include the important lead and silver mining district of Menheniot. Interesting gangue minerals here include calcite, which is rare in Cornwall.

CARN BREA
[SW 685406]

A good viewpoint and place to take in the atmosphere of this part of west Cornwall, looking out over the principal mining district to St Agnes Beacon and the West Penwith hills standing up behind St Ives. Granite tors on the summit exhibit rock basins, such as the Giant's Crocks and Kettles or Cups and Saucers [SW 684407]. Neighbouring Carn Marth [SW 715408] has no tor, but has been quarried.

CARNGLAZE SLATE CAVERNS
[SX 187668]

A dark Middle Devonian slate outcrops in the narrow St Neot valley south of the village towards the Fowey valley and A30 road. It was both quarried and worked underground in places. The disused slate caverns at Carnglaze [Telephone: (0579) 20251] are open to the public during the summer, and contain a huge unsupported roof and flooded pool deep inside. Other underground workings across the valley have been blocked by rock falls.

CARZANTIC QUARRY
[SX 362834]

A small quarry beside a lane, $^3/_4$ mile [1.2 km] NE of Lawhitton, giving an exposure of dipping

Carboniferous radiolarian chert. There are other quarries in this chert with shale partings around Launceston, but many have been filled in.

CHEESEWRING
[SX 258724]

Best approached from Minions village on the south-east edge of Bodmin Moor. The summit of Stowe's Hill has a selection of fine tor formations, of which the Cheesewring is the most famous. There are also some rock basins. Cheesewring Quarry shows the jointing beneath the hill to good effect and how it relates to the surface features. Minerals found here include amethyst, wolfram, pyrite, with the rarer betrandite. The first recorded phenacite in Britain was discovered here in 1905.

This is an area full of tin and copper workings. Immediately below to the east are the surface remains of Phoenix United Mine [SX 267720], a source of mineral specimens although the dumps have been largely removed. A line of pits and shafts follows the main lode to West Phoenix Mine [SX 253721]. It crosses the moor just south of Stowe's Hill, and passes an area of tin streaming at the head of the Witheybrook valley. To the south, copper was worked around Caradon Hill in the nineteenth century and there are extensive remains of mines with waste dumps yielding some specimens at South Caradon [SX 265700], East Caradon, Marke Valley and Wheal Jenkin.

CHINA CLAY DISTRICT

The Hensbarrow granite is the centre of the china clay industry, and the landscape around St Austell, Nanpean or Bugle is forever changing. It is well worth driving around, as some of the large pits can be viewed from public roads, showing the method of washing soft material from the pit face with high-pressure hoses (monitors). The waste tips contain mostly quartz and feldspar. China stone is quarried near Nanpean. The Wheal Martin China Clay Museum [Telephone: (0726) 850362] is at Carthew [SX 005554] beside the A391 north of St Austell. The traditional processes can be seen, such as refining,

A typical china clay works.

Helman Tor. *P.S.*

thickening and drying. Displays include old photographs and tools.

DELABOLE SLATE QUARRY
[SX 075840]

The source of good quality grey slates of the Upper Devonian, Delabole is said to be the deepest quarry in England, at 500 ft [152 m] deep, This huge working quarry was active in at least Elizabethan times and perhaps as early as the thirteenth century. There is a public viewing platform from which the quarry interior can be seen, and a nearby building contains a display of roofing slates, slabs and other slate products currently produced here. Much smaller quarries are active in the Delabole area and at Trebarwith, producing grey and rustic slates.

DEVIL'S JUMP
[SX 102800]

Two pinnacled outcrops face each other across a deep valley, where the stream from Stannon Marsh leaves the edge of Bodmin Moor to flow into the Camel. This and Lanlavery Rock, near Roughtor at SX 156826, are quartz schorl dykes.

GOLITHA FALLS
[SX 224686]

Cascades and waterfalls are rare in Cornwall. This is at a knick point on the Fowey River, where the down-cutting river has been held up by the junction between softer slates and the hard granite margin of Bodmin Moor. There is a good example of river capture here, with the windgap at Redgate. Golitha is now a

nature reserve and there are signposted walks through the woods beside the river. Adits and two waterwheel pits are reminders that minerals have been worked here.

HELMAN TOR
[SX 063616]

This is the only Hensbarrow granite hill with a tor resembling those found on Bodmin Moor. Its craggy outline rises to 687 ft [209 m] on the western side of Red Moor. It is visible from a point on the A30 west of Lanivet, and is well worth following narrow lanes to get there. Massive flat rocks are a feature of the northern end, while the main summit pile includes a logan rock. Just to the south is the perched Cup and Saucer Rock, surrounded by lesser rocks with a logan and rock basins.

KILMAR TOR
[SX 253749]

A superb long east-west ridge of granite tors and the third highest summit on Bodmin

A 'cheesewring' on Kilmar Tor. *P.S.*

The Witheybrook Valley, Bodmin Moor, showing the 'basin and gorge' effect of the main WSW – ENE trending granite structure. The remarkable parallel ridges centred on Kilmar Tor (resistant wide-spaced joints) are matched by river 'gorges' with cols and 'basins' in the weaker granite between. Note abrupt change of the Witheybrook's course at Trewortha Marsh.

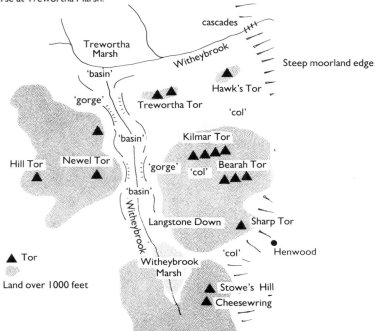

Moor. A fine viewpoint. The best approach is from Stowe's Hill (Cheesewring) or Henwood village, which then takes in Sharp Tor and Bearah Tor, the latter a smaller version with a quarry on the south side. Many of the clitters around Kilmar and Bearah show the marks of stone-cutting in the last century. To the north, the next parallel ridge is lower, with Trewortha Tor (where King Arthur's Bed is an enlarged rock basin) and Hawk's Tor, notable for close horizontal joints which give thin slabs of granite. Note the course of the Witheybrook stream as it passes through 'basins and gorges' from a marsh near Cheesewring, before turning abruptly east to follow the trend of the ridges.

KIT HILL
[SX 375713]

A prominent granite hill near Callington, now a country park. It is much scarred with the remains of mining and granite quarrying. The metamorphic aureole suggests that Kit Hill is connected at depth with the neighbouring Hingston Down granite. There are mines in this district from Callington to the Tamar at Gunnislake and Calstock. They are mostly tin with some wolfram, arsenic, lead and silver, with copper becoming more common to the east. Molybdenite can be found on Kit Hill and in the working granite quarry at Hingston Down [SX 410718].

LUXULYAN VALLEY
[SX 056572]

A unique part of Cornwall, thoroughly 'granite' in character, with huge rounded and half-buried granite blocks on the rough open slopes, in the surrounding fields, and among the trees. Several stones have names, such as the Largest Block in Europe, or Giant Block [SX 061576], which weighs an estimated 1,700

Round granite blocks near Luxulyan. *P.S.*

tons, Pennyloaf, Elephant Rock, Oven Rock and Will Luke's Hat [SX 060568]. The centrepiece of the valley is the impressive ten-arched Treffry viaduct, completed in 1842 with large granite stones for a tramway system connecting the port of Par with quarries, mines and china clay works. The course of the tramway can be followed towards the Carmears Rocks [SX 069564], which rise out of the trees on the east side of the valley near Pont's Mill.

Luxulyan is known to geologists for the unique rock known as Luxullianite, which has large crystals of pink feldspar set in a dark groundmass of quartz and tourmaline. The main source was an isolated surface rock, the Hunter's Stone, which was cut up for the Duke of Wellington's sarcophagus in 1855—6, now in the crypt of St Paul's Cathedral. Luxullianite is most striking when polished and examples can be seen in the Geological Museum, South Kensington.

RED DOWN
[SX 262855]

Just south-west of Egloskerry, Red Down is part of a high ridge of Lower Carboniferous chert which extends east towards St Stephens (Launceston). A lane and the route of the former London & South Western Railway make use of a gorge cut by the River Kensey through the high ground [SX 276858]. A tributary flows through another steep-sided valley which separates Red Down from Tregeare Down [SX 250863]. Several roadside quarries give exposures of the dipping beds of chert.

ROCHE ROCK
[SW 992597]

A strange group of rocks, unlike anything else

Roche Rock. *P.S.*

Rosemanowas Quarry, Hot Rocks scheme showing the injection and production wells. August 1982

in Cornwall, stands out from a moor just north of the china clay district near Roche. The rock is a quartz schorl, an altered granite with small crystals of white quartz and black tourmaline. The ruined St Michael's chapel (1409) stands on the main rock, which is about 60 ft [18.3m] high. The surrounding rocks are strangely sculpted.

ROSEMANOWAS QUARRY
[SW 735346]

This former quarry was the scene of the Hot Rocks geothermal research project in the 1980s, where the boreholes enabled water to be pumped deep into the granite below, to be returned at a high temperature, raised by the natural heat of the rock. The site is in Cornwall's largest granite quarrying district, where the landscape around Stithians, Mabe and Constantine is scarred with old 'dimension' stone quarries and their waste tips. Not far away, Carnsew, Chywoon and Haws quarries now produce crushed stone.

ROUGHTOR
[SX 145808]

A classic tor formation, surrounded by clitter-strewn slopes and reached by easy walking from a car park at end of a lane from Camelford. There is a good logan rock on the main summit. Showery Tor is an interesting formation at the north end of the ridge. The whole is a good viewpoint across much of Cornwall from north to south coasts. Note the nearby china clay workings at Stannon Pit, a reminder that not all the granite here is everlasting. The 1,000 ft [305 m] erosion platform, mostly within the metamorphic aureole, forms an extensive area 2 miles [3.2 km] north on Davidstow Moor [SX 155840]. Roughtor's neighbour, Brown Willy, is the highest point in Cornwall [SX 159800].

In the same parish of St Breward, and near that village, granite is quarried at De Lank, Hanter-gantick and Tor Down.

ST CLETHER ROCKS
[SX 203845]

Lavas in the metamorphic aureole are exposed

as outcrops along the sides of the Inny valley north-west of the church. They can be approached from the footpath to the holy well and chapel.

ST KEW ELVAN DYKE
[SX 015768]

The lane leading west from St Kew village towards Chapel Amble follows the top of a narrow ridge, steep on the south side. This has been formed by an elvan dyke where it has proved more resistant than the surrounding Upper Devonian slates into which it was intruded.

TRURO CATHEDRAL
[SW 826449]

Hardly missed in the centre of Truro, this tall cathedral was completed in 1910. It is included here because it provides an example of many buildings which are of geological interest. Cornish stones used in the structure, fittings and memorials include granite, serpentinite, Pentewan stone, Polyphant stone and Delabole slate, while there are also 'foreign' stones from other parts of Britain and abroad. A small leaflet is available as a guide at the cathedral. When visiting Truro, the mineral collection at the County Museum in River Street should be viewed.

Truro Cathedral. *P.S.*

Glynn Valley china clay works, Bodmin Moor. *P.S.*

FURTHER READING

Barton, R.M.	*An Introduction to the Geology of Cornwall* (Bradford Barton, 1964)
British Geological Survey	Map sheets at 1:50,000 (formerly one-inch) scale, with companion Memoirs describing the geology in great detail (for complete list, see Edmonds, *et al*)
Cartwright, A.	*Truro Cathedral Rocktrail: A guide to its building and ornamental stones* (leaflet, 1989)
Dearman, W.R., Freshney, E.C., King, A.F., Williams, M. & McKeown, M.C.	*Geologists' Association Guide No. 10: The North Coast of Cornwall from Bude to Tintagel* (1970)
Dines, H.G.	*The Metalliferous Mining Region of South-West England*, 2 vols (HMSO, 1956)
Edmonds, E.A., McKeown, M.C. & Williams, M.	*British Regional Geology: South-West England* (HMSO, 4th edition, 1975, reprinted 1985)
Embrey, P.G. & Symes, R.F.	*Minerals of Cornwall and Devon* (British Museum, 1987)
Ferris, L.C.	*Pebbles on Cornwall's Beaches: identifying and collecting* (Tor Mark Press, 1969)
Hall, A.	*Geologists' Association Guide No. 19: West Cornwall* (1974)
Hosking, K.F.G. & Shrimpton, G.J. (eds)	*Present Views of Some Aspects of the Geology of Cornwall and Devon* (Royal Geol. Soc. of Cornwall, 1964)
Kirkaldy, J.F. & Bates, D.E.B.	*Field Geology, Minerals and Rocks* (New Orchard, 1988)
Perkins, J.	*Geology Explained: Dartmoor and the Tamar Valley* (David & Charles, 1972)
Robson, J.	*'Cornish Mineral Index'*, Trans Roy Geol Soc Cornwall, vol 17 (1948), 455–475.
Smith, J. R.	*Cornwall's China Clay Heritage* (Twelveheads Press, 1992)
Stanier, P.	*Cornwall's Mining Heritage* (Twelveheads Press, 1988)
	The Work of Giants (St Ives Printing & Publishing, 1988)
Thurlow, C.	*White Gold From Cornwall and Devon: An illustrated account of the modern china clay industry* (Cornish Hillside Publications, 1992)
Woolley, A.	*Guide to Minerals, Rocks and Fossils* (Hamlyn, 1989)

Good bookshops will be able to obtain copies of these books that are still in print.
Local libraries can help locate older titles.

Front cover: The Cheesewring, Bodmin Moor.

ISBN 0 906294 22 3   © P. H. Stanier 1990. Second impression (with minor amendments) 1994.
All rights reserved. No part of this publication may be reproduced or transmitted in any form or by any means without the prior written permission of the publisher.
First published 1990 by Twelveheads Press, Chy Mengleth, Twelveheads, Truro, Cornwall TR4 8SN.